The Little Blog of Lucanus

How we brought the Good News to Rome

Onwards and Upwards Publishers

3 Radfords Turf, Cranbrook, Exeter,
EX5 7DX, United Kingdom.
www.onwardsandupwards.org

This first edition published in the United Kingdom by Onwards and Upwards Publishers (2017).

ISBN: 978-1-911086-84-0
Typeface: Sabon LT
Editor: Ruth Noble
Graphic design: LM Graphic Design

Printed in the United Kingdom.

Endorsements

Simon Ratsey has produced a wonderfully original take on the travels of Lucanus (better known to most of us as the writer of the Gospel of St Luke and the Acts of the Apostles). The blog idea makes it both concise and engaging. We are given a real flavour of what it was like in those early days of Christianity, before lofty buildings, liturgies, robes and stained-glass windows began to define the Church, as opposed to simple goodness and faith in a loving God. I wish this book great success. It deserves it.

Nick Butterworth
Author and illustrator

In this well-researched book, Simon brings to life the events of the early days of the Christian church. The characters from the biblical story of Acts are fleshed out in such a way that their personalities become alive. The addition of details about the period and the imaginative insights into living in those uncertain times add to the authenticity of the biblical account. An enjoyable and thought-provoking read.

Dave Bishop
Simply Church Ministry, Consultant to Churches
Former Leader of Yeovil Community Church

Simon takes the reader on a journey that will both inform and inspire. It's a story that is earthed in faith.

The Right Reverend James Jones KBE
Bishop of Hull (1994-1998) and Bishop of Liverpool (1998-2013)

About the Author

Simon grew up on a dairy farm in Somerset, which gave him both a love for and an understanding of the countryside. With rural life being greatly influenced by the weather, he began keeping daily temperature and rainfall records in his youth, developing a life-long interest in graphs and statistics. Also having an affinity with words, at school he was actively encouraged in creative writing, in due course enjoying academic success. Studying Geography at the University of Durham, he became both a Christian and an environmentalist, at a time when those two were unusual, and sometimes uncomfortable, bedfellows. After serving in the secondary education sector for nearly twenty years, he reconnected with nature and became a freelance gardener for the next twenty-five.

Since retirement, Simon has once more enjoyed having the time to undertake a variety of writing projects. As well as carrying out serious scientific research on weather and climate, he has written short papers examining biblical themes, mainly for his own benefit and satisfaction. He always finds the Bible to be a rich source of ideas and inspiration, prompting questions such as "What does it really mean?" and "What was it really like?"

For the past thirty years, Simon and his wife Anne have lived in Wellington in Somerset, where they are active members of the local church. Simon is also involved with several community groups, balancing time spent indoors writing with time spent outdoors, volunteering on a local nature reserve or working in his own garden.

Acknowledgements

Writing can be a slow process, and four years have elapsed since I drew up my first list of bullet points about the Book of Acts. Most of the people who have played a part in the creation of this book are unaware of their involvement, so I record my gratitude to them now.

At the start, I must thank my English teachers at Wellington School in the middle of the last century, who insisted on grammatical accuracy as well as creativity in writing. Having tentatively taken up my pen again in later life, I offer my thanks to Bishop James Jones and to Rev. Dave Bookless, both of whom gave useful hints, as well as encouragement to keep writing. Likewise, thanks to my long-time friend Dave Bishop for his ongoing support.

The format for this book came by inspiration when I was watching David Suchet's fascinating BBC TV documentary "In the Footsteps of St Paul", while for both theological and historical material, I owe a debt of gratitude to Bishop Tom Wright for the wisdom shared in his "Acts for Everyone" books.

When I began having doubts about the value of what I had written, it was Rev. Steve Jenkins, at Life Central Church, who urged me to find a publisher. Since then I've enjoyed the enthusiastic support and exemplary professionalism of Luke Jeffery and his team at Onwards and Upwards Publishers. Thank you all for helping to make a long-term dream come true.

Finally, special thanks to my wife Anne who read an early draft of the book and said that she enjoyed it. She exhibited patience with me to a very high degree during the production process. I can do no less than dedicate this book to her, with my sincerest love.

Author's Note

From the Age of the Classics, we have a famous legacy of myths and legends that tell of the exploits and adventures of an assortment of great heroes. But it might be argued that among the most significant (but least appreciated) adventure stories from the past is one founded in fact and written down nearly two thousand years ago. It chronicles how one man, with a small and changeable group of companions (who wouldn't have seen themselves as heroic), willingly faced hell and high water on a mission to spread the good news of a world-changing event, from its place of origin in a minor province of the Roman Empire to all corners of the known world. And it's in the Bible.

These days there are many for whom the Bible is a closed book, and so they miss out on at least one really engrossing story. But it's also probably the case that many who are quite familiar with the contents of the Bible have no clear mental picture of precisely what happened when and where, as the cultural shockwave of the Christian message spread out from its epicentre in Jerusalem. This phenomenon is described in the section of the Bible we call "The Acts of the Apostles". Much of it deals with the activities and encounters of various small groups of men who saw themselves as being on a mission from God, during a series of journeys by sea and by land in the middle of the 1st century AD. Very helpfully, further information about their life and times (including useful cross-references) is supplied by the various letters or "Epistles" also included in the Bible. Most of these were written to the earliest communities of followers of Jesus of Nazareth, in some cases by people who had been friends or relatives witnessing the things he'd said and done. The writings of some ancient historians in Rome also help to create a context for the narrative. Collating information from these various documentary sources allows the construction of a fairly clear picture of what may have been going on in a very challenging period in the history of the Roman Empire.

My purpose in writing this book is first to have created a "good read". In the process, as far as possible, I've tried to set known facts in chronological order, as well as to spell out some of the key teachings that accompanied the spread of the astounding news that the man known as Jesus of Nazareth had risen from the dead – and all that that implied.

There is fairly strong evidence someone referred to as "Luke" was an eyewitness to some episodes recorded in "The Acts of the Apostles", and he's widely recognised as the author of that book as well as of the Gospel that bears his name. His style of writing indicates that he was a highly intelligent man, with considerable powers of observation and a thorough approach to his research. He certainly left us enough factual information to reconstruct a fascinating tale.

Exercising a fair amount of artistic licence, but in keeping with our times, I've chosen to retell part of Luke's literary legacy in the form of an edited diary. That device permits the use of concise modern language, which, I hope, will make the story easier to follow. Any reader who may choose to cross-reference with the biblical texts will have no trouble identifying the fictional elements. Such additions are intended to enhance the continuity as well as the credibility of what must have been a truly memorable series of adventures. Anything in a footnote is a modern addition inserted to aid understanding.

Finally, readers of a certain age may recognise my nod in the direction of the late actor and storyteller David Kossoff, one of whose highly enjoyable works was "The Little Book of Sylvanus". If I can even approach his narrative skills I shall be more than satisfied.

Simon Ratsey
Wellington, Somerset
July 2016

Contents

PREFACE

In my youth, the last thing I would have imagined was one day being called upon to write a book about my own life. But life has a way of throwing up surprises. It's been a long life, too, and now that I'm well past my "threescore and ten" I've been persuaded that my adventures, as well as the amazing stories I've been told, need to be properly recorded for posterity. It's fortunate that my diaries have been in safe-keeping over the years, giving me memories as fresh as on the day they happened.

Just clearing things up at the start as to who I am, I'm normally referred to as "Luke" or "Loukas" in the communications sent out by my friends. However, when in Rome, do as the Romans do, and I got used to being called "Lucanus" in the years that I spent in that city. But I've been living in Corinth for a while now, reunited with friends and with the rest of my diaries too. I'd left them with dear Chloe, who (rather cheekily) read them all, and it was she who has urged me to turn them into a book for all to enjoy. It's been a demanding task, but it has revived lots of memories of dear people and fascinating places. I hope that the result of my efforts gives you at least a taste of the eventful life that stretches behind me.

PROLOGUE

All Greek to Me

My involvement in the story that I'm about to tell resulted from a series of amazing coincidences, although looking back it seems as though they were simply part of a divine plan. Certainly, in view of the circumstances of my birth, I could never have imagined the life of adventure that lay ahead.

I've visited many great cities over the years, and have almost come to love Corinth, teeming multicultural metropolis that it is. Even so, Syrian Antioch, on the banks of the Orontes River, is the place I've always thought of as home. It is a beautiful city, and important in its own right for both trade and culture. In my youth I used to take for granted such world-renowned sights as the Street of Colonnades and the Temple of Artemis. However, one always appreciates the familiar things far more with hindsight.

I think I was born in the seventeenth year of the reign of Augustus Caesar[1], who was hailed as the greatest ruler the world had ever known. As everyone in his expanding empire was well aware, he'd been officially proclaimed "Son of God and Saviour of the World" – a world in which all people would know the benefits of Pax Romana. Be that as it may, while I was growing up I was not aware that the Emperor had any real influence on my everyday life. I was told that when I was still quite small he ordered a census to find out the total number of people

---

[1] 10 BC

under his rule in the provinces of Syria and Judea, fairly recent additions to the empire. (He was reputed to have loved lists of facts and figures, which may explain in part why he left his regime in a far better state of administration than he found it.) My mother and I were simply listed in the census as "slaves" in the household of one Anaxagoras, an Athenian. My dear mother was the kindest person I ever met, but she would never tell me where our family had come from originally. I came to suspect that there was some dark or shameful secret in the past.

Anaxagoras was well-off, having made the move from Athens to Antioch as a young man, in the hope of making his fortune in the commercial sector. In this he had succeeded, becoming prominent in local business and on the City Council. He always recognised the basic equality of men, treating his staff well, and allowing me to receive an education alongside his own two sons. (They said my father had died of a fever when I was still a baby.) Having spent his formative years in Athens with its renowned obsession with "ideas", my master was a thinking man, though with little time for religion. "There are just too many gods," he would say with a chuckle. "Show me even one that really does any good!"

I turned out to be a better student than either of the other boys, so rather than have my talents wasted in serving at table, for instance, Anaxagoras arranged for me to go to medical school so that the family might have its own doctor. (This is still quite a common practice, and physicians who have a good grounding in the teachings of Hippocrates are always highly sought-after.) I appreciated my master's generosity, and made the most of my studies. As part of my training, it was recommended that I kept a journal, mainly for recording people's ailments and the treatments that worked (or didn't, as the case may be). Gradually, I got into the habit of including all sorts of other bits of information about my daily activities – for which I've since been very glad. Memory alone can let one down.

Life in Syrian Antioch was on the whole quite agreeable. I wasn't aware of any real lack of freedom, and was encouraged to maintain friendships with some of the others whom I'd got to know at medical school. They weren't all slaves like me, and a few of them came from very wealthy families. Occasionally I would hear tales of their visits to other cities and provinces, and that did make me sometimes think it would be a wonderful experience to travel farther afield than simply moving between Antioch and the coast when the family took their holidays. And it was during one of these holidays that a tragedy was narrowly averted.

The event remains vivid in my memory, and changed the course of my life, occurring in the same eventful month that the late and very much lamented Augustus was succeeded as Emperor by his adopted son Tiberius. I was twenty-three, and beginning to gain more of an understanding of how the world worked. There was a widespread sense of optimism as this Tiberius, though no longer young, had a great reputation both as a soldier and a governor. Little did we know the sort of tyrant he would become – but that's another story.

Back to our seaside holiday. My master's elder son Anakletos, two years my senior, had grown into a very agreeable young man with excellent prospects, although I felt (professionally, of course) that he was unhealthily inclined to overindulge at the meal table. His parents had previously failed to find him a suitable match, but he was at last engaged to be married to a lovely girl whose family had come from somewhere in Macedonia. He was also about to be appointed as a co-director in the family business. One warm summer's evening, Anakletos became violently ill, suffering repeated spasms of agony in his stomach. As he sank towards what seemed certain death by morning, accusations flew that he'd been poisoned, with fingers pointing in all directions. (Poisoning was a popular topic of conversation with the spread of rumours that the aged Emperor Augustus had met his end that way.) Distraught family members begged me to save him, at any cost. While naturally I didn't want to lose the nearest thing I had to a brother, I knew also that my reputation as a physician was at stake.

I don't know what prompted my thoughts, but I realised that Anakletos might have eaten something a bit suspect in the huge mixed seafood platter that he'd polished off at the midday meal. "Accidental poisoning" was what crossed my mind. I looked up a certain herbal remedy I'd been taught for some types of gastric problems, found I had the necessary ingredients, and hastily mixed a potion.

With the trembling patient held in his father's arms, I brought the cup to his lips, but he convulsed and knocked my hand away. At the second attempt, I managed to pour a reasonable dose down his throat. Nothing happened at first. Then with a shudder and a groan, he vomited violently and sank back motionless. Had I killed him? It would be my death too. But no. After a few moments we saw him take in a deep breath, and soon after that he opened his eyes and gave a rather weak, wan smile to a group of mightily relieved onlookers. The experience had clearly taken it out of him, and after he'd been given a good clean-up he was allowed to rest, although his mother never left his side. In the morning he woke up and said, "I fancy some figs," which seemed to do him no harm, and within two days he was fully fit, enjoying his holiday again (but being a bit more cautious about what he ate).

That's how I became a free man. My master Anaxagoras said he couldn't repay me enough for the miracle I'd performed, although I saw it as just an inspired hunch followed by prompt treatment. In the months that followed I stayed close to the family (and my mother), but was now given licence to pursue my career in medicine in the wider world. With a new reputation that had gone before me in the city, I quickly acquired quite a long list of regular clients. One other most gratifying result was that I was invited to join the gentleman's drinking club in the city, the Symposium.

Symposium was a great place for discussing all things philosophical and theological, even if the vast quantity of wine that was regularly consumed meant that patterns of thought could wander quite erratically, often with humorous consequences. (Although one of my teachers at medical school had maintained that a good laugh might cure all manner of ills!) In any case, I was always a listener rather than a talker. It was there I first began to hear about the god of the Jews – the one whose name should be neither pronounced nor written down. I have to admit that the only god I'd previously given much thought to was Asclepius, the god of healing, and that was purely out of professional interest.

One of the Symposium members returned from a business trip to the Jews' capital city, Jerusalem, in Judea province. As it was his first visit, he was struck by the enormous contrasts between their culture and society and ours. Of course, I'd known of Jews in Antioch, but I had almost no contact with them in the normal course of life. Some people called them lazy, because on a certain day every week they wouldn't do business, or work of any sort. One got the impression that their religion was very exclusive, that they considered themselves a chosen race who would one day rule the whole world. That sort of arrogance didn't help them make friends or gain acceptance in the community. Nevertheless, having grown up with so many different gods and goddesses, I found the idea of a whole nation having just one all-powerful creator god to be quite intriguing. And the Jewish concept of a god who actually cared about his people really challenged my thinking! All the deities I'd known of seemed highly temperamental, a person's main priority in life being to avoid at all costs doing anything that might upset them.

While my own interest in what the Jews believed was superficial, this was not the case with Nicolas, a good friend of mine at Symposium. The younger son of a wine merchant in the city, he was a man of sharp wit and unquenchable good humour, but became a diligent student of the ancient Jewish writings. After a while he regularly joined a local group of Jews when they gathered at their community hall on the non-working day, or "Sabbath" as they called it. He seemed to find the teaching there very interesting, often excitedly trying to explain to me new things that he'd learned. "You're a thinking man, Loukas! Consider the evidence!" he would say. "When you read the prophets of old you can tell they knew what they were talking about, and they foresaw a wonderful future. For generations, the Jews have been carefully counting the years. Now, right across the empire, there's this rising sense of anticipation that certain world-changing prophecies must soon be fulfilled – but it hasn't happened yet! Doesn't it get you excited too?" Well, at the time, I certainly needed more evidence than he could offer.

In the end, he himself became a believer in the "Great and Only Lord God", submitting to the uncomfortable initiation ceremony of circumcision that gave him Jewish identity. To my regret, he resigned from Symposium, and went when possible to Jerusalem, particularly for the major religious festivals. I met him occasionally when he was in Antioch, always full of new stories about what he'd seen and done on his travels. He told me about the awe-inspiring Holy Temple in Jerusalem, still in the process of being rebuilt to ever higher standards of splendour and extravagance. There was a certainty in the minds of many Jews that it was the building where the Lord God would soon come to live among His people, as the scriptures foretold. At its very heart, he explained, was the Holy of Holies, the place where heaven and earth met. The High Priest alone was permitted to enter it, on just one special day in the year, and only after much ritual cleansing and the offering of sacrifices. Even then, there was no guarantee that he wouldn't be slain by the Divine Presence, and a long rope was attached to his ankle so that his body could be dragged out, if the worst happened...

While I admired the zeal of Nicolas for his new-found faith, I personally didn't find this god with the unutterable name a very inviting prospect after all, and my level of interest in the Jews and their beliefs soon declined. Gradually, Nicolas and I met less often, and as the respective courses of our lives diverged we eventually lost touch altogether. Besides, there were lots of people needing a doctor, and I was kept busy with my expanding practice.

News of a Revolution

Many years would pass before Nicolas and I were to meet again. I continued to go to Symposium, but not as regularly as before. I built up a wide circle of friends and acquaintances through my work, Mother delighting in the way I seemed to have broken the fetters of a fatherless child brought up in servitude. She urged me to find a good wife – sometimes several times a week! Finally, when I was almost thirty years of age, I very nearly married the younger daughter of one of my more prosperous clients, who was enticing me with a considerable dowry. Then I found out that she was carrying another man's child. It was a very sad situation, as she'd been betrothed to him but he had died suddenly only days before the agreed wedding date. I'm not sure I would have made a very good father. People said that her family connections would help me move up in society, but it didn't seem at all right, and my heart was certainly not broken by the ending of the arrangement. My heart did break at the sudden death of my mother, some ten years later. She had been a devoted servant in the same household all her life, and everyone greatly mourned her passing.

One death that few lamented was that of Tiberius Caesar, whose reign had been peppered by episodes of political infighting and murder, as well as frequent public discontent. Considering the number of enemies he had made, it was remarkable that he survived into his late seventies. He'd left Rome in the hands of a couple of unscrupulous sidekicks, living in self-imposed exile on the island of Capri, where by all accounts he spent his last days in miserable debauchery and violence. For better or worse (and it turned out to be the latter) he was succeeded[2] by his great-nephew Gaius, generally referred to by the nick-name "Caligula". Following what has become normal imperial practice, messengers were sent from Rome to all corners of the empire carrying the good news of a new ruler, one of whose titles was the now hereditary one of "Son of God". I knew that to be something that the Jews really resented, though I didn't at the time understand why.

A few years before that, a quite different news story had reached Antioch, from Jerusalem. Apparently, there had been some very strange events there around the time of the Jewish Passover festival (their most important religious celebration), and again during the Feast of Pentecost that came some weeks later. That brought my old friend Nicolas to my mind, for the first time in ages. For a while, a highly implausible and confusing story from Jerusalem was the focus of much of the gossip in some quarters of the city.

The word going around was that the Roman authorities had publicly executed a carpenter from Galilee District, a rather poor rural area in Judea province, for allegedly trying to start a revolt during the festivities in Jerusalem. There was nothing very remarkable about that. It's well known that there has always been tension between the Jews and the Roman "occupiers" in that city, and such disturbances happen from time to time. It's also well known that the Romans habitually use crucifixion as the punishment for anyone rebelling against their regime, and executions are commonplace. In this particular method the condemned man is publicly stripped, flogged half to death and, to put it bluntly, nailed up on a tree. The practice is considered so degrading and agonisingly painful that it is against the law to use it on any Roman citizen.

What was so different, in this instance, was that far from trying to stir up an armed rebellion, it appeared that the carpenter in question had gained great popularity and a wide reputation as a teacher and miracle-worker, who proclaimed a message of peace rather than war. He'd had a fair-sized band of followers who could say nothing bad about him. Now some of these friends were reportedly going around asserting that this carpenter-prophet had come back from the dead and, in various locations in the province, had met and even shared meals with people who'd known him. It was claimed that on one occasion he'd been seen by hundreds of people at the same time, before finally vanishing from the earth in strange circumstances. I didn't know what

---

[2] in 37 AD

to make of it all. It wasn't a new idea, gods being resurrected from the dead – but not a human being…

During the weeks and months that followed, stories were being circulated about all manner of supernatural things happening in Jerusalem – life-long cripples being miraculously healed, and so forth. The new leader of the alleged rebel group (also from Galilee District) was reported to have declared that it had all been foretold by prophecies in the Jewish sacred writings. The man who'd come back from the dead was the "Messiah" appointed and anointed by their God to establish the eternal kingdom of heaven on earth. He, not Caesar, was the one who had rightful claim to be called the "Son of God". At last, this man had proclaimed, it was what the Jews had been waiting and longing for, for generations.

It didn't sound very credible to me (I mean, dead carpenter to immortal king!) and all the evidence pointed to life continuing much as before in the administration of the provinces. In fact, periodic "good news" proclamations from Rome suggested that the youthful Gaius Caesar was doing all he could to strengthen his grip on his empire, and with an almost fanatical zeal. The rumour from Rome was that some people close to him were suggesting (strictly in private, of course) that he was showing signs of madness. Being "Son of God" was not enough, so he'd declared himself to be a god in his own right, even ordering a statue of himself to be erected in Jerusalem so that the Jews could worship him there. That would indeed have been mad. The riots that would have inevitably ensued didn't happen, however, as for once he paid heed to his advisers and, at the last minute, changed his mind.

Then, one very windy day when I was trying to push my way through the crowds in Antioch city centre, I literally bumped into Nicolas. In spite of both of us now having greying beards, we recognised each other straight away. It was wonderful to see him again, looking so well, and with the same cheeky twinkle in his eye. Suddenly I realised how much I'd been missing him. He had lots of questions for me, and said that he himself had really exciting news to tell, so I invited him back for a meal.

As we ate and drank, he unfolded quite a tale. It turned out that for more than ten years he'd been based in Jerusalem, involved in the local wine trade. On the whole, it had not been a bad place to live, apart from the ever-present and greatly loathed Roman army of occupation, which kept everyone's nerves on edge. Nicolas spelled out to me the situation as he saw it. "The Jews are still hanging on to the promises in their scriptures that the Lord God is soon going to set them free once and for all, and give them a leader who will rule the world. So, being in effect slaves to Rome is a constant source of anger and frustration. Having their own national 'king' doesn't help at all. The general public regard his family, the Herods, as outsiders anyway, and he's tolerated by Rome only because he makes it easier for Caesar to tax the people. In Jerusalem, especially, the Jews' religion and their sense of national identity go hand in hand, so there's always been a rebellious element in the population. Their history has been dotted with outbursts of violent protest against a succession of pagan foreign rulers. But it's a story of one disaster after another."

Nicolas told me in great detail about the latest so-called rebel leader, Jesus of Nazareth. Yes, he was put to death by crucifixion, followed within a matter of days by the astonishing reports of his very much alive appearances to lots of people who'd known him well. "Jesus wasn't a rebel in the normal sense," he explained. "He may have been a carpenter by trade, but he was also a well-educated Jewish rabbi, held in high regard, especially by the lower classes, and always more than happy to party with anyone. There were religious leaders who denounced him on the grounds that this was no way for a respectable rabbi to behave, but he didn't pay them much attention. His stance was that the Lord God loves everybody equally, including those often viewed as the dregs of society. What he taught often turned upside down what people had been brought up to think. But when he spoke it was with an amazing authority, and people would travel great distances to listen to him. I heard him myself more than once. Some people even hailed him as a prophet cast from the same mould as the greatest ones who had spoken for the Lord in the distant past. And he could out-reason the cleverest legal and theological experts, often telling them that they simply didn't understand what the scriptures really said."

Here I interrupted him, saying, "Wasn't that rather tactless of him?"

He laughed. "Oh, I'm sure Jesus put a lot of people's noses out of joint, but that didn't seem to bother him. He told great stories as well, often witty and packed with meaning, and he sometimes pinpointed those he called the religious play-actors as the butt of his jokes. He taught that we should love our enemies, though I didn't really understand how that would work out in practice! And he backed up his words with actions – for instance, I'm told he not only actually touched people with leprosy, but that they were healed as a result. And there are eyewitness accounts of him bringing dead people back to life, including one of his good friends."

"Really? That's incredible!"

"Yes. And as that is the sort of thing that God alone can do, Jesus was seen by some as declaring himself as a rival god, a blasphemy punishable by death under the Jewish legal system. Things really came to a head when word got around that he was coming to Jerusalem for the Passover Festival. He always attracted crowds anyway, and when he appeared riding into the city on the back of a young donkey, this was seen as a reference to one of the ancient prophecies about the arrival of the Messiah in the Holy City to liberate the people. They said that the crowds were cheering as though he'd already got the Romans on the run! But after a few days in the city, with Jesus showing no indication of planning to lead an armed revolt, public opinion became divided about him. The atmosphere grew unusually tense, with a recent failed attempt at an uprising still fresh in people's minds. This seems to have finally convinced those in power that Jesus was such a destabilising influence on society that they should silence him once and for all. In the event, the Jewish and Roman authorities actually joined forces in this, with a show trial and public execution. Most of his friends went straight into hiding, thinking that they'd be next in line to get similar treatment. Of course, it all backfired, as subsequent events have shown. With Jesus believed by many to be alive again, and with the authorities totally unable to produce a body or prove in any other way that he is still dead, more and more people have been convinced that everything claimed about him being the Messiah must be true!"

The stories of further supernatural happenings during and after the Feast of Pentecost had not been invented, he said, with visiting Jews from all corners of the empire being witnesses to what took place. Men who'd been afraid to show their face in public just a few weeks before were now speaking out boldly in the city centre. It was a turning-point in history, they declared. The words of the prophets had come true, and from now on everything would change. In the light of that, there were claims that it was no longer necessary to make sacrifices to receive forgiveness for sins committed, or for any other reason, for that matter. Some people could see how the astonishing sequence of events had added a whole new complexion to the Jewish faith. Moreover, it was now possible for any individual to experience the presence of the Lord God, in complete safety, and without even needing to be in the Holy Temple. That kind of message didn't go down very well with the authorities, as it was seen as a grave threat to the established rule of law. And the last thing the Jewish rulers wanted was to give the Romans any excuse for imposing even more oppressive measures on the population.

Nicolas also described to me how there came to be a growing rift between two distinct groupings of pious Jews. On one side were those who believed that Jesus the Galilean carpenter-rabbi really was the Messiah who fulfilled all the ancient prophecies. They often referred to themselves simply as "Followers of the Way". On the other side were those who were appalled at the notion that such a man, humiliated and crucified as a blasphemer and rebel, could be anything other than cursed in the sight of God. They insisted that the Messiah they still expected would be instantly recognisable as a royal descendant of the great King David, and regarded themselves as true "children of Israel", deriding the others as "the cult of the Nazarene". Even though they all celebrated the same festivals and worshipped in the same Temple, there had been increasing levels of animosity between the two sides.

Eventually, for his own safety, Nicolas had needed to come back to Antioch. That was about two years before our chance meeting, so it was a little surprising we'd not met sooner. (He'd had no reason to suppose that I was even still alive after so long, and we were now moving in completely different circles, anyway.) The Jerusalem city authorities had some time earlier launched a campaign to arrest anyone who was a follower of "the Nazarene", or who spoke about the new kingdom of heaven that had been proclaimed. That made Nicolas a marked man, as he'd become a believer too – one of thousands, it seems, including members of the Jewish priesthood.

The more that I heard, the more curious I became. Having been trained to be analytical, I wanted to know the details, and Nicolas was happy to provide them. He described to me how the community of Jesus-followers in Jerusalem was made up of Jews from all over the empire, including many who'd witnessed the strange events at that momentous Feast of Pentecost. Some had returned to their homeland after the festival, taking amazing stories with them. Many others, like Nicolas, didn't leave Jerusalem until things started to hot up later. However, once back home in their various towns and cities, they naturally formed into small pockets of like-minded people, embedded within the Jewish community but tending to see themselves as separate from it. While still adhering to the old traditions and religious observances, they introduced a new one, regularly sharing a special meal together. In this, they commemorated the death and (especially) the resurrection of Jesus, those events being seen as the inauguration of this new era for the Jews. There was great excitement and a sense of anticipation that the Lord God would soon fulfil all the words of the ancient prophets, and at last set up His kingdom here on earth. Not surprisingly, a lot of people were getting very interested. (I did wonder whether this news might have reached the Emperor's ears...)

Something that really intrigued me was the way these Jesus-followers seemed different from the general population of Jerusalem. It sounded as though they lived as a distinct but very inclusive community, eating meals together in one another's homes, sharing their belongings with one another, and even selling property to raise funds to put in the general kitty. With many expatriates from all corners of the empire there, some people were quite dependent on any handouts that were available. People being people, it wasn't long before there were disturbing allegations that financial support wasn't being distributed fairly. To deal with that, seven men had been selected to form an administrative team to oversee such practical matters, Nicolas being one of them.

"Things had been going well," continued Nicolas, "and, on the whole, Followers of the Way were getting quite a good reputation for the positive impact they were having on life in the city. Some of the religious leaders, on the other hand, still felt they were being undermined, with the purity of the Jewish faith now seriously compromised. Then one day we were horrified to learn that Stephen, one of my co-workers, had been arrested on a charge of 'behaviour likely to cause a breach of the peace'. Now, everybody knew that Stephen was a man of highest integrity. Nevertheless, with scant regard for legal protocol, the High Council of the Jews found him guilty of blasphemy against the Lord God Most High. They condemned him to death by stoning, and promptly carried out the execution themselves without any reference to the Roman authorities. The whole tragic business stank! In the wake of that, the High Council instigated a general persecution of followers of Jesus, with no shortage of people willing to do their dirty work for them. Our leaders – those who'd themselves known Jesus well, called the Apostles – said that all of us who hailed from other parts should get away from Jerusalem if we could. They stayed put, prepared to face the music – which they did, from time to time. The local ruler had one of them executed, and would have done the same to Simon Peter, the Apostles' leader at the time, had he not been miraculously freed from prison by a mysterious messenger sent by the Lord."

I couldn't help being struck by the note of excitement in Nicolas's voice as he told me his story – one, it seemed, he had shared with many others already. For after returning to Antioch, Nicolas and a couple of his friends had spoken at the local synagogue[3] on several occasions. They felt that the news they had was so important that every Jew in the city should hear it. There was a very mixed reception, he said, with a lot of opposition, and accusations of heresy from some traditionalists, while others just laughed out loud. Some, however, accepted that it did seem to agree with what the prophets of old had foreseen, and were prepared to take things further.

I felt that this very thought-provoking story should be shared at Symposium, and said so to Nicolas. His response was, "If you can arrange that, I'll be more than happy to accept the invitation!" A couple of days later, I was able to speak to Anakletos who'd taken his late father's place on the City Council. After checking with others, he said that Nicolas, as a former member and respected friend, would be most welcome at the next week's Symposium. It was to change my life.

Far from being a lone voice, Nicolas found that by chance he had an ally there, a very articulate Greek Cypriot named Androcles, who had also witnessed the events in Jerusalem. He and a friend Simeon from Africa were visiting Antioch, taking every opportunity to share with anyone and everyone the news about Jesus the Galilean who'd risen from the dead. Apparently, quite a number of folk had been persuaded that it was true, and there were now small pockets of non-Jewish Followers of the Way scattered throughout the city.

Listening to them there, and considering what I'd learned from the Jewish scriptures, I began to feel that their reasoning was starting to make sense. I'd never come across people who were so convinced that what they believed was the real thing, and they spoke with the passion of men possessed. And if the world was indeed becoming a different place, it was such amazing good news that you really wanted it to be true! As I thought things over late that night, it was as though a voice spoke inside my head, addressing me by name, asking me to follow him too. I didn't understand at the time.

---

[3] Jewish community centre

25

The Good News Goes Viral

Having re-established my friendship with Nicolas, I couldn't help coming into contact with other people in his circle, many of them now believers in Jesus. Each of these could tell his (or her) own story of a life that had been transformed by him – or more accurately by his Holy Spirit, who, they said, changes a person from the very core of their being. (This was something I understood very little about, at the time.) It became fairly obvious in just a few years that many aspects of life in Antioch were undergoing a strange transformation, something that people noticed and commented on with interest.

The changes stemmed from the fact that a growing number of people had taken to heart the message about this Jesus of Nazareth who'd been raised from the dead to inaugurate an alternative kingdom. They now wanted to live according to his rules based on practical love. The economy picked up, which was great, as it had been flagging a bit, and there was a new buzz in community life. People stopped trying to cheat each other in business, and groups of families pooled their resources so that nobody lacked food or clothing. When it was realised that a lot of people didn't have a family at all – widows and orphans especially – an outreach programme was started up. Even people who didn't have a lot themselves contributed money, clothing and food for those who were worse off. And believers from both Jewish and Greek backgrounds were treating each other as equals (which infuriated some of the die-hard Jews).

It became quite normal down on the banks of the Orontes River to see groups of all ages celebrating, as new believers were given a ceremonial dunking, or "baptism". I'd heard about this long-established Jewish ritual, a public way of saying goodbye to the old life and starting a new one lived in accordance with the laws of God. Only now, people were being baptized in the name of Jesus of Nazareth too. I found my mind being pulled in different directions. I wanted what these seemingly renewed people seemed to have, but I had my own circle of friends, my position in society, my profession… But from time to time, especially in waking periods in the night, I seemed to hear a voice in my head, gently calling, "Loukas! Loukas! I'm still waiting for you!"

It was on the morning after one of these sleepless episodes that Simeon knocked on my front door. (Simeon was the African whom I'd first encountered at that crucial Symposium meeting, now highly regarded as a leader of the Followers of the Way in the city.) "'Morning, Brother Loukas!" he said cheerily. "I understand that you didn't sleep well last night." (How did he know that...?) "The Lord Jesus has given me a message for you. He says that he's still waiting for you, and has great plans for your life. And he doesn't want you to stop being a doctor!"

I didn't know what to say. Waves of different emotions flooded over me, before I was able to cry out, "If he really wants me, then I don't see that I have any choice!" Cutting a long story short, before that day ended I too had been baptized in the waters of the Orontes, and formally welcomed as a brother into the "family of Jesus", as Simeon put it. I felt a completely different person, although I couldn't really explain it in words. I would understand more in due course.

This marked the start of a period of discovery and great excitement for me. I was hungry to learn all I could about Jesus' life. I made friends with Jewish believers, who mostly turned out to be quite normal people after all, and were happy to explain more about what their ancient scriptures tell us. I met a lot people who'd had a personal experience of supernatural happenings – although they were often very matter-of-fact about them, as though it was to be expected now. Incredible stories were going around about people being healed from diseases simply by the power of Jesus' name spoken over them by his followers. We heard of a girl, only twelve years old, who seemed to have a real gift for that.

I soon learned all about the custom for believers to meet on the first day of the week – the Lord's Day, they called it – and share bread and wine together. (The first time I joined in one of these special meals was also when I first had a sense of Jesus being close to me in person, which was almost overwhelming.) The celebration took place in line with precise instructions given by Jesus himself at the last meal that he'd had with his close friends. That was just before he was arrested in Jerusalem. It clearly made a lasting impression on them.

There was also a sense of anticipation at this meal, as we were reminded that Jesus had said that he would soon be coming back to establish in full God's heavenly kingdom on earth. It was about the same time[4] that we'd received the good news of another Emperor in

---

[4] 41 AD

Rome, this latest one hailed as "Claudius Caesar". (His predecessor Gaius Caligula had apparently gone too far down the road to insanity, eventually being assassinated by his own bodyguards.) However, rather than seizing this as a good opportunity to wage war on the empire, Jesus' followers continued to spread a message of peace and reconciliation – Romans included.

Then a chap called Joseph turned up from Jerusalem. Physically much bigger than most men and with a personality to match, he was "Barnabas"[5] to all his friends. Although from the priestly tribe of Levi, and with his family home on Cyprus, he'd thrown in his lot with the Jesus movement in Jerusalem from very early on, and was now one of the leaders of the community of Jewish believers there. News had apparently reached them about the goings-on in Antioch, and, as a seasoned traveller, he'd been sent off on a fact-finding mission.

It wasn't long before Barnabas was pleasantly reassured that the "Antioch Experience" was totally in tune with the "Jerusalem Experience". He met and spoke with many of the new believers in Jesus (including me), his message being always along the lines of, "Stay firm in what you believe, and stick with Jesus the Messiah[6]." With a voice to match his physique, and a thorough understanding of the Jewish scriptures, he addressed a good number of meetings in the city, and many more people became convinced of the truth about Jesus. With Antioch having good links with most other major cities in the eastern half of the empire, it wasn't surprising to learn that the "Good News" (as it was increasingly termed) was beginning to spread farther afield.

After three months in the city, Barnabas held a meeting with the leadership team of the main group of Followers of the Way (or "Christians" as some people had rather sarcastically started to call us). He said he knew the man who was best qualified to instruct us all in our new faith – a first-rate intellectual and former stickler for the purity of the Jewish faith, who himself had suddenly and dramatically become a believer in Jesus. Barnabas explained how he had first met this remarkable man in Damascus, very early on, and had then introduced him to some of Jesus' friends in Jerusalem. He'd been very active in spreading the "Good News of the kingdom" in the region for about three years, before the Jewish authorities caught up with him and he

---

[5] "Son of Encouragement"
[6] Christ

had to flee to his hometown of Tarsus in Cilicia province[7] where he'd since been effectively in exile. Barnabas felt it right to now go and find him.

Some weeks passed and then Barnabas returned, accompanied by a very short, slightly-built man immediately recognisable by his clothing as a Jewish rabbi. His piercing dark eyes were set in a face that was lined beyond his thirty-five years of age, and his black beard was trimmed neatly to a point, suggesting a man who liked things to be "just so". His name was Saul, and his arrival caused Nicolas to almost explode with anger.

"You must be joking!" he shouted at Barnabas. "Don't you recognise who this man is? He's the reason why I had to come back here to Antioch! He was there in Jerusalem giving his approval when they murdered Stephen! He would have had us all killed if he'd got his hands on us!"

Barnabas placed a large hand firmly on Nicolas's shoulder and pressed him back into his seat, saying, "Please calm down, my friend. Let our guest speak for himself, and then make your judgment."

It was some while before Saul had finished his story, and by the end of it no one there doubted his integrity. It was a fascinating tale that I would hear many more times in the years that followed.

Named after his royal ancestor in the Tribe of Benjamin, Saul had been born into a well-to-do family with an established leather-working business in Tarsus. His Jewish ancestors, linen weavers by trade, had moved there many years before to take advantage of the large quantities of flax grown in the area. His grandfather had diversified into leather goods, supplying the imperial military machine with a wide range of products, especially tents, and one result was that the family had been granted Roman citizenship. Tarsus is in many ways like Antioch – for many years a very peaceful, multicultural city, with numerous different religions happily co-existing. And with its renowned School of Philosophy, there could hardly be a better place than Tarsus for a young man to receive a first-class education.

Notwithstanding, from childhood Saul had been brought up in the tradition of the Pharisees, a particularly strict Jewish sect. His mother had died soon after giving birth to a daughter while Saul was still a toddler. His widowed father had great aspirations for him to pursue the career in religious law that he himself had been denied, so a couple of

---

[7] south-east Turkey

years after his "bar mitzvah" (coming of age) Saul was sent to Jerusalem to undergo training as a Pharisee. Very soon he was awarded a place in the school of Gamaliel, one of the most revered teachers at the time. Under him, he studied how to be absolutely scrupulous in obeying all the laws and commandments set out in the scriptures, and zealous in persuading others to do the same.

(Over the years since then I've learned quite a bit more about the Pharisees, which has helped me understand why some of the things Jesus taught upset them so much. They believe that if all the people will live completely pure and blameless lives, God's promised Messiah will at last come to establish the nation of Israel in its rightful place above all other nations. Then, at the end of the age, both the living and the dead will have to face judgement before the throne of that same Messiah. Those judged to have lived sufficiently worthy lives will receive immortal bodies and live for ever in a newly recreated world. According to their tradition, the Messiah will come to earth on a sacred mountain near Jerusalem. It is a favoured burial site for pious Jews, who hope to be among the first to greet him when he arrives. I never imagined that I would one day myself set foot in that special place.)

Saul related to us how, as a zealous Pharisee, he had indeed conducted a hate-war against what he regarded as the heresies being spread by the cult of the Nazarene. In that context, he'd been on his way to Damascus in Syria with authorisation to arrest any followers of Jesus he found there, when he had a life-changing experience. He explained it in terms of a personal encounter with the Lord Jesus, which left him temporarily blind but permanently convinced that he had been selected as the one to take the Good News to every corner of the empire.

After that, he'd had to do an awful lot of rethinking of what he thought he knew, and spent over a year on retreat in Arabia before going back to Damascus. When he did finally return to Jerusalem he was a changed man, but the followers of Jesus there didn't believe what he said, and would have nothing to do with him. This was where Barnabas came into the frame, acting as intermediary and bringing about a meeting that cleared the air to a large extent. Saul described how he then joined in the work of preaching about the risen Jesus, until the Jerusalem authorities started to close in on him, at which point some friends smuggled him home to safety.

He may have been a tent-maker by profession, but it didn't take us long to recognise Saul's real gift. Even in the fiercest of debates, he was the quickest thinker I'd ever met, adept at turning other people's arguments on their head with his impeccable understanding of the Jewish scriptures. He and Barnabas stayed with us for a whole year, helping to establish the "ecclesia"[8], which is how they referred to the community of people who believed they'd been called by the Lord Jesus to spread the culture of his new kingdom. One person who became a believer as a result of meeting Saul was a young man called Titus. His mother, it turned out, was my own dear mother's niece, and I was delighted to find out that I had relatives! He became a close friend of Saul, who spent a lot of time teaching him one-to-one.

In spite of the distance, Christians from Antioch would sometimes go to Jerusalem, and vice versa. One group who visited us included a young man named Agabus who had a special gift of prophecy, and he declared that a severe famine was going to take place (which in fact did happen, quite early in the reign of Claudius[9] when he was back in Rome after overseeing the annexation of the new province of Britannia. When I asked someone where it was, they replied, "Oh, somewhere way beyond Gaul. Really cold, and rains all the time, they say. I don't know why anybody would want to go there...") We agreed to take up a collection among the Christians in Antioch on behalf of our fellow-believers in Judea province, and entrusted the money into the hands of Barnabas and Saul. They were both very keen to see their friends and relations in Jerusalem again. Saul also felt that it was very important to get his message across to his fellow Jews on their home soil.

It was several months before they returned, accompanied by a very youthful-looking man in his mid-twenties called John Mark, whom I understood to be a relative of Barnabas on his mother's side. As a boy, this John had apparently met Jesus during some of the latter's visits to Jerusalem. I was very interested to hear what he had to say, but found him most reluctant to talk to me. When I mentioned this to Barnabas, he explained that John had been brought up in quite privileged circumstances in Jerusalem, and had never had much personal contact with non-Jews. In view of my own background as an "outsider", I was given to understand that he probably felt quite torn in his loyalties – conscious of his Jewishness, but knowing that it shouldn't matter now that we're all in the Christian family.

---

[8] church
[9] about 45 AD

Barnabas and Saul had much to tell us about their visit to Jerusalem, and it's hard for me to remember many details now. However, we understood that Saul had spent time with some of the key men in the church there, certain misunderstandings from the past having been finally resolved. They'd advised him not to try to meet members of the High Council of the Jews, or other religious leaders, as they were sure he would be rejected by them, at the very least. He'd apparently accepted this as wise counsel. My main concern at this period became Saul's health. While away, he had become subject to frequent and often severe abdominal pains, which left him feeling weak and sometimes very short-tempered. Even prayers for healing spoken over him by Jesus' friends in Jerusalem (normally so effective) made no difference.

My expertise as a physician was called upon, and although I couldn't identify a precise cause for his suffering, I suspected irregular eating habits. It was well known that Saul might go for many hours at a stretch without food or drink, if engrossed while teaching and debating. After trying out various possible remedies, I found one particular herbal potion that seemed to tackle the acute symptoms quite effectively – to everybody's relief. I thought that Saul was joking when he said that from now on, wherever he went, I'd be going too.

Six weeks later, John Mark came to see me with a message from him: I should pack my bags, as I would be going on a journey. A bit of a shock, I must admit. Probing him for more information, I learned that the five senior leaders in the Antioch church had recently spent several days in prayer and fasting, with the outcome being a clear instruction from the Lord Jesus to set apart Barnabas and Saul for a special project. With a support team, they were now to take the Good News of the risen Jesus and his kingdom to other parts of the empire. Suddenly, it seemed, there was a sense of urgency that Jesus would return before many people had had the chance to hear what was going to happen. Barnabas wanted John Mark in the mission team, and Saul was insistent that I went as well.

Before agreeing, I spoke to the man face-to-face. Not surprisingly, he used his verbal gifting to talk me around to his point of view without much difficulty. I then set my own terms: I didn't know how I'd take to travelling, and might find I needed to return home. In the meantime, I was happy with the invitation to be his personal physician, and I'd willingly keep a diary of our travels – but stand up and speak to an audience? No thank you! It was all agreed, and that is how all that follows came to be written down.

TRAVEL DIARIES – SERIES I

March 17[10]

Much hugging taking place in the Antioch church, as our travel party of four prepares to leave. There are very mixed feelings here over the departure of two such key personalities as Barnabas and Saul, with no guarantee that any of us will be coming back. The general idea seems to be to head for Rome, taking in other towns and cities that may happen to be on our route. First, we're to go by boat to the port of Seleucia, about twenty miles down-river. There we shall board a Cyprus-bound ship, which we've been assured will be waiting for us. Simeon and Titus are coming down too, to see us off. I think I'm quite excited about the prospect of having an adventure, at last! John Mark has of course never been to sea, either. We certainly don't feel afraid.

March 19

We managed the short journey to Seleucia in one day, but with the wind in totally the wrong quarter for setting sail we have had to find lodgings for a couple of nights, at least. This afternoon I took the opportunity to visit a nephew of my former master Anaxagoras, and met his young and very pretty wife too. They were delighted to receive the latest news from the Antioch branch of the family. Barnabas has just confirmed that we have seats booked on a small cargo vessel, which will be returning to Cyprus to load up with wine.

---

[10] 46 AD

March 23

At last we're at sea, with a very favourable breeze. The ship's captain thinks that we should make landfall on Cyprus early tomorrow, and we hope then to seek out some relatives of Barnabas who are also believers. So far, the journey has been quite enjoyable, and I was thrilled to see a group of dolphins, which I've only ever heard about in some of the old stories. They travelled with us for some distance after we left port, often leaping and slapping their tails in the water as if excited at being our escort.

March 24

We've arrived safely at Salamis, on the east coast of Cyprus. Although the sea was a bit rough for a while, nobody got seasick. Saul was very excited to be at last on his way, and hardly stopped talking, locked in discussion with a group of Jewish Cypriots on their way home. They wanted to know why this little rabbi was going on a sea journey. When told the reason, they said they'd not yet heard of this "Jesus of Nazareth". But we know that reports about him were brought here some years ago, by Androcles among others.

Saul wasted no time in getting to the heart of his message: "In Jesus of Nazareth, a bit of heaven was walking around among us here on earth. Through him, the Lord God demonstrated His power and authority over all creation, in full view of everyone! By raising Jesus from the dead, God showed that he is the promised Messiah, who now reigns with God in heaven, and on earth too – his Holy Spirit lives in us and works through us! But Jesus will be returning at any time. This means the end of the world as we know it is coming, and we've all got to make ourselves ready for that!" I could tell that some of his hearers were astonished beyond words by these claims. They didn't know whether to believe him or not – it sounded crazy, but Saul clearly displayed a profound understanding of their scriptures.

I'm now really getting to know John Mark, who's become much more friendly and keen to talk. ("Call me 'Mark'. Everyone else does!") It sounds as though he was right in the thick of things when Jesus made his final visit to Jerusalem at that fateful Passover, and he wrote down what he saw happening at the time because it seemed so important. He's been telling me a lot more about Jesus' background too, and giving detailed accounts of some of the amazing things he did. I hope that in time I'll be able to meet some of the others who knew Jesus personally. Meanwhile, Barnabas has arranged for us to lodge with some of his relations here in the town for as long as necessary. There is a large Jewish community here, so I expect Barnabas and Saul will find themselves being kept very busy. Even though the Good News is for everyone, they feel that it is right to share it first and foremost with the Jews – the ones Saul keeps referring to as "my brothers".

March 27

Barnabas, Saul and Mark have been in one of the local synagogues all day. I chose to spend my time exploring the area. Met some very friendly locals, who wanted to know where I was from and why I was here – which led to a long and involved discussion, but they seemed really interested in what I was able to tell them about Jesus. Glad of my past experience at Symposium, but quite worn out afterwards! Saul has just returned with the others. Complaining of his pains again – I doubt if he's taken a proper meal break today. I'm always urging him to remember to take a little wine for the sake of his stomach. Anyway, it seems the day was well spent, as they've been asked to stay on and address meetings at the other synagogues.

April 5

On the road again, at last. Barnabas feels that we should be pressing on, if we're to reach Paphos on the west coast while the weather is set fair for sailing. Our route is taking us along the southern side of the island, with occasional glimpses of the Great Sea stretching to the horizon and shimmering in the sun. Already we have passed luxurious groves of trees, with beautiful scenery on all sides, and wild flowers galore! I've recognised some very useful herbs, including chamomile and peppermint, and am restocking my medicine chest whenever I get the chance. Having failed to find anywhere to get lodgings for the night, we're for once sleeping under the stars, but the air is from the south, warm and fragrant with blossom.

April 10

Very unpleasant for travelling, with a strong north wind and bursts of heavy rain. I've never in my life been so cold and wet! We decided not to try to reach Paphos today, and will be staying overnight here at this rather comfortable old inn. It has one wall decorated with a fine mosaic of the god Dionysius, which Saul has taken as a very good pretext for quizzing the innkeeper and some of the other guests on which gods they serve… I expect he will be quite late to bed.

April 11

Arrived in Paphos before noon, and had a look around after some rest and refreshment. Our first impression: a city in which the worship of the goddess Aphrodite is pre-eminent, with all the licentious behaviour that goes with it. Fertile ground for our message! The Jewish quarter is fairly small.

April 14

Still in Paphos. The weather has improved, but we know we'll be stuck here until there is a favourable wind. Saul feels that if we can just get to Rome, that'll be our best way of spreading the Good News through the whole empire. This morning we were back in the Jewish quarter, where Saul had a serious confrontation with a strange man known locally as Elymas, hailed in the area as a very clever magician with alleged powers of spiritual insight. He reacted angrily at the Good News of Jesus the Messiah, and said that he'd be reporting us all to his boss for trying to make trouble in the city. Mark has seemed a bit subdued after this – I think he imagined that everyone who heard the Good News would receive it wholeheartedly.

April 15

Elymas's boss turns out to be Sergius Paulus, the Roman governor, by reputation an intelligent, fair-minded man (even if his idea of a joke isn't always in the best of taste). Earlier today he sent a summons to Barnabas and Saul, as he wanted to hear what they had to say that was causing such a stir. The two of them came back this evening with this interesting tale:

An attendant had shown them into the governor's office, introducing them as "Josephus" and "Saulus". As they stood before him side by side, Barnabas towering over Saul, Sergius Paulus[11] exclaimed, "Hail, Maximus and Paulus! One man and his puppet!" Elymas, one of several other attendants in the room, had apparently laughed inordinately loud and long at this. (Barnabas said that he was amazed at the way Saul had kept his composure.) While showing due respect for the governor's status, Saul had proceeded to explain the Good News to him, with Elymas repeatedly interrupting and saying things like, "Don't listen to him! It's all rubbish!" In the end, Saul had had enough, faced him eyeball to eyeball, and called him a son of the devil who was trying to pervert the truth of the Lord. As punishment, the Lord would strike him with temporary blindness!

That is exactly what happened, and Elymas was left stumbling around trying to find someone to lead him out of the room. Sergius Paulus, on the other hand, clearly came to regard Saul in a completely different and very favourable light, being immediately convinced by what he'd witnessed. He declared himself to be a believer, insisting that they baptized him there and then, the bath-house being very handy for that purpose. That surely makes him the first ruler of any province in the empire to become a follower of Jesus – a sign perhaps of the kingdom of heaven coming on earth? Barnabas and Saul expect to visit him again before we leave.

Another consequence of today's episode is that Saul has decided to call himself "Paul" from now on. While not at all ashamed of his Jewish name, he feels that his newly adopted one may be more helpful when he's dealing with non-Jews – which he expects to be doing a lot. He also said, "Well, I am after all the least of all the apostles…"

Rather than include all my diary entries for the following ten weeks or so, here is a brief summary of what happened.

No one thought that we'd be staying on Cyprus for long, but with Governor Sergius as our ally we were very well received in Paphos. Many Jews received the Good News of Jesus very gladly, and teaching sessions in the synagogues often lasted well into the night. Paul (I'm quite used to calling him that now) found regular paid employment with a local tent-making business, and Barnabas put his practical skills to good use in helping on a building project down by the harbour. Even

---

[11] "Sergius Small"

John Mark cheered up, having got over his initial reluctance to mix with ordinary non-Jews. Increasingly often he would be seen meeting the local young people, and found that some of them really want to hear all about Jesus. It certainly helped him improve his spoken Greek.

As happened back home in Antioch, the old barriers between some Jews and Greeks started crumbling, with people from every sort of background embracing the new faith of "Christianity". Barnabas and Paul appointed several men and women to be leaders in the churches that had grown up in and around the city. They held regular teaching sessions with them, and in time felt that their faith was solid enough for us to think about moving on.

Sergius showed great interest in the plans for the next stage of our journey, and had suggested that our best strategy would be to sail north to the mainland and then head for the capital city of Galatia province, another Antioch[12]. He had relations there, he said, and he would provide us with letters of introduction. "With its prime position on the Imperial Way," he explained, "Antioch has excellent links with several other major towns that you might want to visit." It wasn't the most direct route to Rome, but we could see that it made sense.

July 1

We've been informed that a ship has just arrived from Attalia in the province of Pamphylia[13] and will be returning as soon as it has taken on its new cargo. There's room for ten or so passengers, so it's been agreed that we should take this opportunity to sail. Barnabas will oversee the packing up of stuff we'll need on the next stage of our journey. Paul hopes to visit two of the local churches to give final words of encouragement.

July 4

A south wind picked up last night, and we were woken very early this morning to get aboard ship as soon as possible. They say we should be at sea for only two days, all being well. I must say, I've enjoyed my time in Paphos, and we are leaving many friends here, including the

---

[12] in modern-day central Turkey
[13] southern Turkey

governor, who has generously supplied us with some excellent locally-made wine. He maintains that there is nothing that you can teach the Cypriots about winemaking, as they've been practising the art for thousands of years already.

July 9

Frustration! Following another change in the wind direction with the sudden arrival of a most unseasonable storm, our journey at sea has not gone according to plan. Yesterday conditions were pretty bad, with pouring rain and strong winds that blew us off course, even though the crew had put out anchors and furled the sails very quickly.

John Mark spent quite a time hanging over the side of the ship, groaning and saying, "I want to go home!" in a very plaintive voice. "Uncle" Barnabas tried to cheer him up, saying that things would soon improve, but Paul wasn't at all sympathetic, telling him to face things like a man. (It worries me that Paul sometimes displays surprisingly high levels of intolerance, especially if he feels that others are not showing the same resolution of purpose that he does. I hope it doesn't lead to trouble.) Later, I persuaded Mark to drink one of my herbal potions, which calmed him down a bit. It's now late afternoon, and we're all mightily relieved that the sea's a lot quieter with the coast well within view.

July 14

Having stocked up with provisions in Attalia, we're heading along the coast towards the city of Perga. This should be only half a day's journey, but the land is low, and marshy at the best of times, and the recent heavy rains have caused flooding on the road in places, so progress is slow. It is also very hot and the air is heavy and damp, which is making us all feel pretty listless. Paul is often now taking over from Barnabas as leader (perhaps he feels he's in home territory), and says that it's our top priority to head inland to this other Antioch. I'm quite looking forward to seeing another place bearing the same name as my hometown in Syria.

July 15

We could see the twin towers of Perga's south gate from quite a distance, and were very glad to finally reach the city. We've found lodgings in a side street not far from the central square. There are some admirable examples of Greek architecture here, especially the temple to the goddess Artemis, and there's a wide stream of clean water flowing down the middle of the main street – something I've not come across before. People don't seem to throw their rubbish into it!

Perga appears to be a very peaceful place, with no obvious signs of a Roman military presence.

July 16

Paul and Barnabas have decided we will after all spend a few days here, hoping for an opportunity to speak at the synagogues. So far, it seems the Jewish leaders can't agree among themselves on this, after Paul gave them some idea of the message that he was bringing. He didn't seem too bothered, saying that he'd probably be passing through again in a year or so, by which time they might want to hear him. His normal enthusiasm is definitely lacking, and I would say that he's going down with some "bug" or other.

July 17

Paul did not sleep at all last night, having developed a high fever. Barnabas, Mark and I prayed with him for a while, but we didn't receive any instructions from the Lord as to what we should do. I stayed with him for some hours after that, and tried various treatments, but nothing seemed to make much difference. This morning, our host's wife took one look at him and immediately said, "Swamp fever! You must get him up into the hills where the air is drier." Since Paul is quite incapable of walking at the moment, it looks as though we'll have to carry him on a stretcher.

July 18

Paul said we were definitely not going to carry him, and that he'd be fine after a day's rest. He was not in the sort of mood to be argued with. We left him to try to get some sleep, the good lady of the house assuring us that she'd keep an eye on him. Barnabas disappeared, I know not where.

I did some more sightseeing in the city with Mark. He seemed rather troubled, and when I asked if there was something the matter, he replied, "Please don't be angry with me, Loukas, but I'm not really cut out for this sort of adventure. I need to go back home." I said that it was not a very good time to give Paul that news, but better to turn back now before we get too far from the coast.

July 19

After sleeping on it, Mark has taken the decision to leave us and return home. He's certainly found the going very tough recently. A group from the synagogue is preparing to set off for Attalia, en route to Jerusalem and the Holy Temple, by way of Caesarea. Mark is welcome to travel with them, they say. I'm really disappointed, as he is a very likeable young man, showing great promise. I can tell that Paul feels very let down, and he is clearly in no mood to talk about the matter. Barnabas naturally looks on the bright side, saying that the experience will have done Mark good.

July 20

This morning Paul said he was well enough to travel again, so we packed our bags, and set off for Antioch – just three of us now. To make it easier for Paul, Barnabas had arranged the hire of a donkey, which we will leave for collection at a certain wayside inn in two days' time. (So that's where he went the other day!)

July 23

None of us expected it to be such slow going, even though Paul is now getting his strength back. The air has become much fresher as we've climbed. We thought we'd be heading north, but the very rough terrain means the road, though well paved with stone blocks, is continually changing direction. We passed a great lake, like a sea in the mountains, and there are lots of ravines, which the road spans by means of bridges. These can have ten or more round arches, sometimes two tiers of them, skilfully made with neatly cut blocks of stone. You have to admire the Romans' building skills! To both east and west are high mountains, with large groves of trees on the lower slopes. We have not so far been troubled by thieves, although we were warned that there are many gangs of them in this region. We have made a couple of overnight stops on the way, but Paul seems very keen to get to Antioch as soon as possible.

July 28

Today, we descended from the mountain pass to see the city of Antioch ahead of us in the distance. It's much larger than I imagined, sprawling over a number of low hills on a steep-sided plateau surrounded by rich farmland. The only approach is from the west, where the slope is less steep. The fertility of the land around here is quite a surprise, as the mountain slopes are very bare, suggesting that not much rain falls in this region. I asked a local man about this, at the wayside inn where we stayed last night, and he explained that there are lots of springs issuing from the foot of the mountains, giving a constant supply of water at all seasons. It's reminded me of something that John Mark told me, about Jesus referring to himself as the source of a stream of living water that would never run dry...

August 1

We've settled in at some comfortable lodgings in Antioch, or "Antiocha Caesarea" as they proudly call it. Near the city centre, there's a large carved marble plaque recording how it was Emperor Augustus himself who chose the place to be the administrative capital of the region. There are new streets laid out in the grid pattern that's so common nowadays, and there's evidently been a lot of building in quite a short time. An ornately decorated temple in honour of Augustus "Son of God" has been partly quarried out of a hillside, while the city's main street runs through a tunnel under the side of the 12,000-seater amphitheatre. The city also has clean water flowing in pipes fed from an impressive aqueduct that was built some years ago. It has the same arched construction as the road bridges we crossed. Recently, a new bath house was built here, and we've all enjoyed a good soak after our journey. Luxury indeed!

Besides the large number of serving soldiers in evidence, lots of military veterans have retired here, so it's obviously a very pleasant place to live. As a result, there is much less of a "Greek" feel than I'm used to in a city. Its importance as a focal point is indicated by the presence of people from all different parts of the empire. There's been a prosperous Jewish community here for many generations, and Paul seems to feel quite at home. I can understand why he now regards the city as strategic in his mission to spread the Good News.

August 2

As usual, Paul and Barnabas have made contact with the leaders of the Jewish community, and are hoping to be granted leave to speak at the synagogue this coming Sabbath. I spent several enjoyable hours today with members of the College of Physicians, picking up some new medical skills that I'm sure will prove to be useful. They also hold an excellent library, and have invited me to use it for my own study purposes, which I shall be doing. One exciting piece of news is that some traders have recently arrived from the east bringing, among other rarities, a large quantity of zinziber[14] for sale. This spicy root I have found very effective as a digestive aid, along with peppermint, but it's much more expensive and not often available.

August 5

The meeting at the synagogue went really well, with quite a number of non-Jews there too. As a visiting rabbi, Paul was invited by the synagogue leader to share any message of encouragement he might have for the people, and, needing no second bidding, delivered what Barnabas refers to as the "Standard Declaration". I've now heard it quite a number of times, it being a well-polished resumé of God's dealings with the people of Israel since they were delivered from slavery in Egypt. Familiar to all Jews with even a basic education, the narrative goes something like this (though in much more detail):

"Once settled in their promised new homeland, the Jews were for many generations ruled by a very varied succession of kings who frequently failed to acknowledge their God, or listen to the prophets who spoke for Him. The second of these – King David – was by far the greatest and most significant in Jewish history, and the writings of the prophets declared that when the Lord God finally established His

---

[14] ginger

kingdom on earth, in which His people would live at peace for ever, it would involve a male descendant of David."

By referring to the scriptures – and this is when the story starts to become challenging to Jewish ears – Paul explains how everything points to that promised "Son of David" being the one known in his lifetime as Jesus of Nazareth.

"It was, however, foretold by the ancient prophets that we, God's own people, would fail to recognise him as being the Chosen One, even though latter-day prophet John the Baptizer had warned us of his imminent arrival. We handed him over for execution, only for him to come back from the dead – again in fulfilment of the prophecies – with many witnesses to the fact. That's why we're here today sharing the Good News that what God promised to our fathers has become a reality for us, the children.

"In short, the consequence of all this is that because Jesus is still alive, there is now the possibility of renewed direct contact between God and His people – in fact, all people. The resurrection of Jesus marks the start of a new era in human history, with the inauguration on earth of the kingdom of heaven in which all things will ultimately be renewed. The need for sacrifices and the scrupulous adherence to an infinitely detailed law code has been done away with. Amazingly, it's now possible for anyone – Jew or non-Jew – to receive forgiveness for sins simply by believing in Jesus as the 'Christ'. And woe betide the man who rejects that gracious offer!"

These last statements are simply outrageous to many Jews. They know how they've struggled for generations to maintain the purity of their faith in a pagan world – and now someone's come on to the scene declaring that outsiders are credited by God with a status equal to their own! Paul knows from experience that there's likely to be a backlash. He has, of course, seen things from both sides. As a warning, he often finishes with a quotation from one of the prophets, to the effect that some people will refuse to believe the wonderful things that the Lord God does among them, even if the truth is staring them in the face.

Although he often starts off with a bit of a stammer, once in full flow Paul always delivers a powerful message, and it seems that today's was no exception. He and Barnabas had difficulty getting away from the synagogue after the meeting, with so many people wanting to find out more. There's an invitation to speak again at the next Sabbath.

August 6

I went down to the marketplace to stock up my medicine chest, and couldn't help noticing how many people were talking about what had been going on at the synagogue. My impression is that a lot of non-Jews are getting really interested in the gossip.

August 12

Several of us went down to the synagogue with Paul and Barnabas this morning, to find the building already full and a huge throng waiting outside, as though the whole city had converged on the one spot. With the majority being non-Jews, this seems to have angered the leaders of the synagogue. Their whole attitude had changed and they began to abuse Paul and contradict what he was saying. Maybe Paul's digestion was playing up today, for he very quickly lost patience and said, "That's enough! You've made your feelings quite plain. We felt that it was right and proper first of all to bring this Good News from the Lord to you, our Jewish brothers and fellow children of Israel, but now that you seem bent on rejecting it – and disqualifying yourselves from the promise of eternal life – let's see how everybody else responds!" And then, being Paul, he promptly backed up his stance by quoting one of the prophets who had said that "salvation" would be made available to all people on earth, not to the Jews only.

Standing on a low wall so that he could better project his voice, he began to address the assorted throng around him. It was an amazing demonstration of both his depth and breadth of understanding of the scriptures. There was no shortage of eager listeners in the crowd. By this evening many had taken to heart the message they heard about Jesus and how he was raised from the dead, to set up a heavenly kingdom on earth that anyone who put their trust in him might enter.

August 15

We had to pack up and leave in a hurry yesterday. A very strong reaction from the leaders of the Jewish community in Antioch means that we are no longer welcome in the city. Rather than arresting us all, the city police marched us far enough away to no longer pose a threat to law and order there. Paul and Barnabas have, however, managed to hold several meetings with groups of non-Jews in the past week or so, and are satisfied that a lively community of Christians is already established. Paul's attitude towards the Jews here now seems to be, "Well, if you don't want us around anymore, that's your loss! Let's see what kind of reception they'll give us in Iconium[15]."

August 17

Stayed at a very fine inn last night, where we enjoyed the company of a party of Jewish merchants on their way from Iconium to Antioch. Barnabas was explaining who we all were and why we were travelling, and mentioned that I was a doctor. One of them was then pushed in my direction, as he had a very painful sore on his leg. He said it resulted from an insect bite, and it didn't seem to want to heal at all. Surprisingly (or perhaps not, in the circumstances) he was happy to be treated by a non-Jew, and I was able to apply an herbal poultice. Even by this morning he was delighted to report much less discomfort, and I could see that it was looking better. While we chatted, he mentioned that he had grown up in Tarsus. When I told him that it was also Paul's hometown, he was very pleased. "You'll be needing lodgings in Iconium?" he asked. "When you get there, ask for my cousin Eleazar. He's got a big house, and I think he'll be really interested in what you have to say. I'm sure he'll put you up."

Don't you just sometimes have a very real sense that the Lord is going on ahead of you!

August 19

For all the reasons one may have for not liking the Romans, we have to applaud them for their roads, not least the Imperial Way. Thanks to this excellent highway we've completed the eighty-mile journey to Iconium in four-and-bit days, without really having to exert ourselves. Instead of the challenging mountain passes we faced on the first part of our trek, the landscape is rolling countryside with villages and farms – all in all, very prosperous-looking. The air is pleasantly cool and fresh, especially early and late in the day. We've found Eleazar, who's pleased to hear from his cousin. Just as we'd been told, he simply oozes friendship and hospitality. His is a large town house, and he's offered us the use of a whole wing for as long as we want, refusing to accept any

---

[15] Konya in modern-day Turkey

payment. He's a devout Jew, and like many others, has been longing for God to fulfil his promises and restore the nation of Israel. Not surprisingly, Paul's teaching about Jesus being the Messiah foretold in the scriptures has already fired up his interest.

August 22

Barnabas and Paul feel that we should expect to stay in Iconium for some time. They hadn't realised just how many Jews live here, so they're anticipating a full programme of meetings. The Jews are the mainstay of the weaving industry here, an important part of the local economy, so Paul thinks he should be able to get some paid work without difficulty. He doesn't seem to mind that we're now getting further away from Rome – but a lot nearer his home in Tarsus.

August 26

An exciting time in the synagogue this morning. Barnabas and Paul were both in great form, sharing the Good News of the kingdom and convincing a large number of the people with their eloquence and detailed knowledge of the Jewish scriptures. As in Antioch, the Greeks and other non-Jews are very keen to find out what is causing such a stir, so Paul has found himself being asked to speak to different groups in all sorts of places in the city. We might well be here for some time.

September 1

Although some people here are eager to give Paul and Barnabas money to help them with their mission, as always the policy is for us to pay our own way. Paul is already helping out with a local tent-making business, Barnabas has again found a good job on a building project, and I've agreed to assist in the practice of one of the town's better-known doctors, who's been exceptionally busy following a fever epidemic recently. It looks as though many evenings are going to be taken up with meetings, as there is no shortage of people wanting to learn more about Jesus.

September 5

Vicious rumours have been spread in the area that what Paul is teaching undermines what is written in the sacred Jewish scriptures – blaspheming the very words of the Lord God. This is very worrying, and we've discussed whether it would be wiser for us to move on, but Paul says that the Lord Jesus has now made it clear to him that we are to stay for the time being, and keep spreading his message without fear. The advice is, "Be prepared for miracles!"

September 24

Our usual morning time of prayer became unusual today. There were about ten or so of us, including some new believers. One young man, Nicomedes by name, who was baptized a couple of days ago, had suffered a broken ankle as a child, leaving him lame ever since. As we were praying, Barnabas suddenly announced, "Nicomedes, the Lord says that your foot is healed – now stand up!"

After a moment's hesitation, the lad in question stood up, adjusted his balance and then shouted out, "It's true! It's true! Look – it's straightened... I can jump!" And he did. He didn't know whether to laugh or cry.

Not surprisingly, our time of prayer turned into a time of praise and worship. That's not the first healing miracle that's happened here, but it is one of the more dramatic ones.

October 7

We had a lively meeting in the synagogue today, several Jews receiving healing for various ailments. One softly-spoken old gentleman said afterwards that he had been resisting the teaching about Jesus, but this time sensed a voice speaking into his heart, and he'd asked out loud, "Is that you, Lord?" Immediately, his fingers which had become twisted by chronic disease straightened out to the full length – for the first time in many years. He couldn't wait to get back home to tell his family that Paul's teaching about Jesus really is true.

October 27

Paul was in full flow addressing a crowd in the marketplace today – not many Jews there – when a young woman pushed her way to the front with a small boy, four or five years old, in tow. She shouted at Paul, "If this Jesus has risen from the dead and is now king of the world, surely he can heal my son who has been deaf and dumb all his life!"

Far from resenting being interrupted, Paul simply fixed his gaze on the woman and said, "Surely he can! Your faith has made it possible!"

Immediately the boy clapped his hands over his ears and cried out to his mother in astonishment. You could almost see a shockwave pass through the crowd.

Paul simply said to them, "The message is the same for you all – believe on the name of Jesus the Messiah, and you will be made whole. More than that, you will be made a new person, because his Spirit will live inside you!"

The uproar that followed is hard to describe, some people being convinced and others shouting about witchcraft.

October 29

It seems that the poor people of the city are the ones who are receiving the message about Jesus most wholeheartedly. Today Paul and Barnabas had to face a throng of street dwellers, some begging for alms and others asking for healing from their disabilities and diseases. At the same time, there seems to be a growing number of the Jewish citizens turning against the new teaching, and I'm concerned that Paul's bluntness in dealing with other people's points of view may land him in trouble. Nevertheless, with news of further amazing healings, there are many from all backgrounds who are proclaiming that Jesus must be the promised Messiah.

November 25

Last night we had the winter's first fall of snow, an unusually heavy one according to the local people. Snow on the mountains is normal, they say, but there's been nothing like this in the city for many years. With everything under a thick white blanket, even sounds seem to be muffled, and it doesn't look as though we'll be going anywhere very soon. I'm very glad that we were not caught by such a snowstorm when out on the open road.

November 30

Life in Iconium has slowed right down, as it's been a struggle to get about. Still, it's encouraging to see how people have been all joining in to help clear the streets, and Barnabas has been excelling with the shovel! Paul has been rather unwell for the last few days, and not very keen to see people, although he's had quite a number of visitors. He's not been eating much, and I suspect he picked up a chill. I'm encouraging him to stay in and keep as warm as he can. Eleazar was getting a bit worried, until I reassured him that Paul is a lot tougher than he looks and is undaunted by difficulties of any sort – and we've had plenty of them recently.

December 14

Everybody is feeling much more cheerful since the snow has finally cleared away, following three days of unbroken sunshine. There's something very comforting in the way everything has returned to normal, and the market was very busy today. Although we didn't suffer any food shortages, it's a relief to see fresh supplies coming in from the countryside again. Paul declares himself perfectly well, and is determined to carry on his project of getting a church established here. This may not be easy. There is a growing difference of opinion between the Jewish leaders on one side, and on the other, those who are choosing to believe the Good News. Worryingly, growing numbers of Greeks seem to be siding with the Jews.

December 28

We thought that things had become suspiciously quiet. Now we know why.
A business colleague of Eleazar has passed on some information about a conspiracy between the Jewish leaders, some of the influential Greeks and the city authorities to arrest Barnabas and Paul at a large gathering they were planning to address tomorrow. Even though it is bitterly cold and late in the day, we are getting all our stuff together in readiness to leave under cover of darkness. Our long stay in Iconium is over. Eleazar

says we're always welcome, if we pass this way again. He's been a true friend.

December 29

We've made it to safety, although I managed to trip over a tree root in the dark, only saved from injury by falling on the bag I was carrying. It was young Nicomedes who showed great initiative in smuggling us out of the city to this isolated farm, about five miles away. Since his healing, he's taken every chance offered to walk or run. He says the farmer and his wife are completely trustworthy. They didn't seem at all surprised at our arrival, and made us very welcome with hot food, and blankets to warm our frozen bodies. Somebody must have made plans in advance for this eventuality.

We've been urged to put some distance between ourselves and Iconium. Rather than get back on the main road for Ephesus, it's been agreed that we'll head for Lystra, a couple of days' travel south from here. Paul thinks we should be safe enough there, as it's a Roman military outpost. All being well, we'll get some good lodgings too, for we're now all heartily sick of being cold!

December 31

We met a Roman cohort as we approached Lystra, presumably out on a military exercise, as we've not heard of any serious trouble taking place in the province at the moment. Until we can make other arrangements, we'll be stopping at this mansio[16] which is basic but comfortable, with heating! Strictly speaking, it's for people on official business, but Paul has used his Roman citizenship (and some clever talking) to get the rules waived temporarily so that we can all stay. The place is almost empty, anyway, so no one is going to be deprived of bed and board because of us.

January 8[17]

Things have been relatively peaceful since we got to Lystra, partly because Jews here are thin on the ground. The synagogue is a tiny

---

[16] Roman roadside lodging house
[17] 47 AD

51

building down a side street. Most of the residents speak the Lycaonian language, a relic of the former kingdom. It's quite hard to understand what they're saying, and so has not been easy to establish the contacts needed for arranging big meetings. I've never been anywhere that is so "un-Greek", with all the places of worship apparently dedicated to Roman gods – some I've never even heard of. There is a local tradition that Jupiter himself once visited, with his messenger Mercury, which probably explains why the temple of Jupiter stands in pride of place at the city gate. Paul usually gets a small crowd around him if he positions himself nearby to talk to people. Since few of the locals are fluent in Greek, and know nothing of the Jewish scriptures, it's been difficult to get across to them the message about Jesus of Nazareth and his new kingdom.

January 12

Better news at last. We have been invited to stay at the home of an elderly Jewish lady called Lois, who heard Paul at one of his little gatherings the other day, and seems to be really excited by the message that the Messiah has come. On a practical level, it means that all of us will be under one roof again, after having been split up among three different homes that were able to offer us bed and breakfast for a time. I've been staying with the family of Julius Crispus, a retired Roman officer, and they've been very interested to know the reasons why we're here. Julius had been a dutiful worshipper of the gods, but only to the extent that it was considered helpful in his former military career. He and his wife have been very open-minded to what I've been able to tell them about Jesus. I've been able to repay them for their hospitality by treating their younger daughter Nerissa, who had a fever. She is much better now, I'm happy to report.

January 15

Uproar in Lystra today! Paul was in his usual spot, not far from the temple of Jupiter, addressing a small gathering. One of the listeners was a crippled man sitting right at the front. He was about thirty years of age, and we learned afterwards that he had been disabled from birth. Paul suddenly paused in his teaching, looked directly at this man and commanded him, "Get up on your feet!" The man promptly stood up and walked around, perfectly straight and upright, with no support.

The effect on the onlookers was astonishing. They started rushing around and shouting, "The gods have come down! The gods have come down! They're among us, looking like people!" Barnabas, being so large, they hailed as Jupiter, and Paul, as the main talker, they took for his messenger Mercury.

Word spread through the city like wildfire, and the high priest of the temple of Jupiter was all set to bring a pair of oxen to sacrifice before them, but Barnabas and Paul were having none of it. Frantically waving their arms, they rushed into the crowd, crying out, "Why are you doing this? Stop it at once, all of you! We're human beings just the same as you! We've come to bring you a message from the living God – that he wants you to turn from these meaningless rituals to him, the one who made heaven and earth and everything in between! He's the one who has always been looking after you, sending rain and ripening your crops, showing kindness even though you didn't know he was there!"

Even so, it was difficult to persuade the people not to sacrifice the oxen there and then, but the event has certainly served to heighten general interest in the Good News that Paul wants to share.

January 19

We have the beginnings of a church in Lystra, at last. Several members of Lois's household have become believers in Jesus, including her daughter Eunice and eldest grandson Timothy. There was quite a celebration today, as seven men and women were baptized and received the gifts of the Holy Spirit. I hope there aren't going to be any difficulties for them. The master of the house, Timothy's father, is a Greek – but he's away from home on business at the moment.

February 11

After a winter that didn't seem to want to end, there's been a great improvement in the weather this week, with definite signs of spring. Conditions for travel should be improving from now on, and we've been thinking that our time in Lystra is drawing to a close. We've made firm friendships here, especially with Timothy. He has got over his initial shyness, and is now actively involved in telling others the Good News.

February 13

Our departure has been suddenly forced on us - in near-tragic circumstances. Word had evidently got back to Iconium and Antioch about the preaching of the Good News here, and a delegation of zealous Jews was sent to sort things out. They've turned public opinion against us, broke up a meeting yesterday, and seizing upon Paul as the ringleader, they stoned him and left him for dead outside the city gates. I wasn't there – we'd been advised to scatter – but as a group of friends gathered around his body, he stood up, brushed the dirt from his clothes, and walked unaided back into the city! As I'd said to Eleazar, he's a lot tougher than he looks.

We're now on the great military road to Derbe, a Roman outpost close to the edge of the province, about four days' journey away. Too far away for the Antioch Jews to harass us, we hope!

February 20

Derbe seems to have welcomed us with open arms. Although smaller than Lystra, it has a larger Jewish community. Paul has plenty of willing listeners, and now that his message is well polished, he's had little trouble getting people to understand the real significance of the death and resurrection of Jesus of Nazareth. Already, more than a hundred new believers have been baptized, including Gaius, Lucius and Demas, who say they want to join in the work of spreading the Good News. Quite a few people have relations in other towns and villages in the area, and they want to take Paul and Barnabas to those places too, when the weather permits.

April 2

I'm heading back home to Syria, and Antioch. The church in Derbe is thriving, and it's time for us to make a move. Gaius is showing signs of being a natural leader, while Lucius has discovered he has a gift for poetry. Some of his works have already been turned into songs of praise and worship for Jesus, and are really catching on.

Now that spring is truly here, travelling will be much easier. We've had several meetings this past week, in which Barnabas set out a number of practical options. There was some discussion about us all taking the main overland route to Tarsus, and then sailing back to

Seleucia for Antioch. Being relatively close to home, Paul was really tempted by the prospect of seeing friends and family again. However, after much prayer and consideration, he said he felt that it was more important to pay a return visit to all the places where he'd preached the Good News of Jesus on the journey so far. It seems that, for the time being, Rome will have to wait.

In the end, it's been agreed that he and Barnabas will return by the longer route with a small team, including Lucius, who wants to go back home to Rome but is looking forward to an adventure on the way. Gaius has been given the task by Paul of overseeing the new church here. Demas, Cyprianus and I will be joining a travel group setting off for Tarsus within the next few days. Pointing out that I'm not as young as the others, Paul has insisted that I take a well-earned break. He thinks that he will be alright without me, but I've given him a good stock of medicine for his stomach, and a stern warning to look after himself properly. I shall miss Barnabas too with his "Never say die!" attitude, whatever situation he finds himself in.

I don't intend to bore the reader with an account of my journey back to Antioch, which was most uneventful compared with life on the road with Barnabas and Paul. Having returned home, it took me a while to get used to not continuously facing the prospect of suddenly having to pack up and leave in a hurry. Little had changed during my absence, although the number of believers in Jesus had grown a lot.

More than a year passed before Barnabas and Paul returned, and I had been praying constantly that the Lord would be with them on their travels. We were all highly relieved when they turned up safe and well. Although they had been back to places like Iconium where they'd been persecuted on their first visit, they said that they were conscious of the Lord's protection all the time. In Perga, where Paul had been prevented by his illness from speaking at any meetings on the outward journey, many people eagerly responded to the Good News. Even the sea crossing from Attalia to Seleucia had a favourable wind the whole way. Talking to Paul, I was struck by the way he seemed to have softened, and said so. His reply was that he'd had a new revelation of the amazing nature of God's love shown through Jesus, and that more and more frequently this was becoming a main thrust of his teaching: "There are some people whom you simply cannot reason into the kingdom – but show them God's love, and it's a whole different response!"

The report they gave to the elders of the church in Antioch caused great celebration. We were now secure in the knowledge that in many towns and cities in Galatia province there were active groups of believers, from every sort of cultural background. Paul and Barnabas had appointed elders to oversee these new churches, as the Lord had directed them. There was general delight and amazement at how the Lord had been at work through them, as they extended the invitation to enter his kingdom to those who had previously been outsiders. Knowing how the young folk need little excuse for a party, it was no surprise that they held one in honour of the returning travellers, although many of us older ones chose not to dance the night away. Where do they get the energy...?

After a while, Barnabas talked about returning to Jerusalem, but Paul urged him to stay, pointing out the amount of "church-building" they still needed to do together in Antioch and the surrounding area. Having spent a year living in close quarters with the pair of them, I'd seen for myself how they'd formed a very strong partnership. I knew that Paul valued the physical presence (as well as encouragement) that Barnabas offered, whatever the circumstances. So Barnabas stayed. Although they always seemed to be very busy, I saw them both quite often in the months that followed.

COMMENT

The Council of Jerusalem

For a long time I had hoped for the opportunity to go to Jerusalem myself, see the places that I'd heard of in the stories about Jesus' life, and meet some more of the people who'd known him as both teacher and friend. I couldn't imagine how this might happen, but needn't have worried. I was heading off in that direction within the year, but before that we were visited by someone who'd known Jesus very well indeed.

Many stories had been in circulation about Simon Peter, who for a while led the church in Jerusalem. The man himself had more recently been keeping out of public view, but with a couple of friends paid us a surprise visit in Antioch, after he'd heard of Paul's return. If ever there was a person to whom the phrase "what you see is what you get" applied, it was Peter. Wrinkled and weather-worn after years as a fisherman, he was much more comfortable speaking his native Aramaic than the Greek that we all tend to use these days. But we soon learned that he had a very good grounding in Jewish scripture, and could preach fluently and with authority. In his no-nonsense approach to the Good News of the kingdom, he said, "If the Lord wants non-Jews like Cornelius to be part of it, then I'll be quite happy to share my meals with anyone!"

Things were fine until a delegation of strict Jewish Christians from Jerusalem descended upon us in Antioch. Peter clearly became very uncomfortable over what they might be thinking about his cross-cultural activities, and he even avoided being seen talking to me, much to my dismay. It became worse when some of the other Jewish members of the Antioch church, including Barnabas, began to change their behaviour in a similar way. I started asking people if they knew what was going on.

Matters had apparently come to a head in Jerusalem. The news was being passed around that many Greeks and pagans in different provinces in the empire were becoming followers of Jesus Christ, but with few conditions being placed upon their inclusion as members of the church. This upset some of the pious Jewish followers there, especially those who had been "religious professionals". I could sort of understand why: concerned over preserving their Jewish heritage, they couldn't imagine how an outsider who had never observed the holy laws and rituals could possibly be in a position to receive any favour from God – let alone experience the new kind of life that Paul and the others had been proclaiming was now available to everyone. Although these purists accepted that Jesus had risen from the dead, thereby inaugurating the "age to come", they nevertheless insisted that unless a man had at the very least been circumcised in line with the custom upheld by Moses himself, there was no way in which he could experience salvation. (It did occur to me that no one in Antioch had ever suggested that I myself should become a Jew if I wanted to be part of the Jesus movement.)

Not surprisingly, this caused trouble, and accounted for the totally uncharacteristic wavering in Peter's stance. In the end, Paul publicly confronted Peter over his double standards. It was quite disturbing to see him being so angry, accusing Peter of distorting the truth – that it's faith in Jesus alone that makes a man acceptable to the Lord God, for the Jew and non-Jew equally. He said, "Look here! If I as a Jew go back to trying to justify myself by obedience to the Law, I make myself as much a sinner as the most ignorant pagan! As far as the Law is concerned, I consider myself to have died on that cross with Jesus, so that, by God's grace, I can share in his new life. If we can achieve righteousness by simply changing our behaviour, then the Messiah died for nothing – and you know that!"

Peter was initially shocked by this tirade, but quickly acknowledged both the spiritual and intellectual authority of Paul, begged forgiveness, and soon got back to normal – to the immense relief of all of us. (I was in due course able to quiz him about "Cornelius", and got a very interesting story which just had to be included in the book about the life and works of Jesus I'd started writing.)

Even though he thought the matter was settled, Paul found himself involved in lengthy arguments with the diehards, neither side feeling it was right to compromise. In the end it was agreed that a representative group from Antioch would go back to Jerusalem with Peter and the others, to confer on the matter with the elders of the church there. Naturally, Barnabas and Paul headed up the group, which was to include Titus, now highly regarded for his faith and godliness, despite his non-Jewish background. To my delight, I was invited to go with them. Paul said he'd missed my company (and skills as a physician) more than he'd expected when I'd left him in Derbe the previous year. Having enjoyed a good break from travelling, I now felt up to the challenge of getting on the road again, and the chance to see Jerusalem was not something to turn down.

After praying with us, and providing gifts of money for the Jerusalem church, our friends in Antioch sent us off. We took the well-used coastal route for part of the way, stopping off in towns and villages whenever we could to share our news with the believers there. Peter seemed to be well acquainted with lots of them. There was often celebration when they heard that people of all kinds, in far-flung parts of the empire, were becoming followers of Jesus too.

From Sidon we struck inland, spending two nights at Capernaum, Simon Peter's home town on the north shore of Lake Tiberias. I gathered that this was one of the first places where Jesus had spoken publicly, the townsfolk being astonished by the level of authority he showed in his teaching. And there were still people there who recalled how he'd restored to sanity and full health a man whom they'd believed to be possessed by a demon. News of that had spread far and wide. From Capernaum we skirted the lake and for three days made rapid progress south on the road that follows the valley of the River Jordan, before heading up into the barren hills towards Jericho.

It was late in the afternoon when we got our first sight of Jerusalem itself – a "wow" moment if there ever was one! High on its hilltop, the Temple of Herod the Great shone as if on fire in the light of the setting sun. Later, when I saw it close up, I realised that some parts of it were indeed coated in pure gold, with building and decorating jobs still going on more than half a century after the reconstruction project had started. Both in its style and extravagance, it surpassed any of the other temples and great buildings I'd seen on our travels. It was awe-inspiring in the literal sense, and I understood in a new way why that sacred place is of such importance to the Jews' sense of identity as a special nation.

We stayed overnight at a house in the nearby village of Bethany (which had been a favourite haunt of Jesus), and entered the city early next day through the east gate. Word of our approach had spread, and we were welcomed with open arms by a group from the Jerusalem church, including, to my delight, John Mark. They were really thrilled by the gift of money we'd brought from Antioch, as times had not been easy following the famine. They were eager to hear first-hand accounts of all the wonderful things that the Lord had been doing through us, so had hired a hall and laid on a meal for all who could attend. Unfortunately, among those present were some who'd been in the very strict Pharisee party, and they started repeating their demands about the absolute need for circumcision, and adherence to the Law of Moses. This rather spoiled what should have been a very enjoyable occasion, and I saw signs of stress in Paul. When I checked with him later that he was taking his medicine, he said yes and that I shouldn't fuss...

It was decided to arrange, as soon as possible, a formal conference at which all the local church leaders would consider and debate this issue that threatened to cause a permanent rift between groups of believers. I was to be there on Paul's recommendation, as he felt strongly that the proceedings should be recorded in writing. He'd already spoken to the man who was going to chair the meeting, telling me later that this was James, a younger brother of Jesus himself, greatly respected even by non-believers for his piety and wisdom.

(It hadn't always been like that, I later gathered. Having grown up in the same family, he bore some resentment towards Jesus who always seemed to be somehow "special", even though all the children were treated equally. Then, when Jesus gave up his carpentry business to travel around spreading the news that God's kingdom was at last being established on earth, he was among the first to accuse him of having taken leave of his senses. Everything changed after he apparently had an encounter with Jesus after he had come back from the dead – but no one knows what each had said to the other then!)

On the day of the conference, I made a point of arriving early enough to get a good seat in the appointed meeting-room. As the seating was arranged in two concentric circles, it didn't really make much difference where I sat. I chose a seat in the front row, and watched with interest as other people arrived. I was surprised at the number and variety of men (but no women) turning up, with some who were clearly very wealthy citizens of Jerusalem happily seating themselves beside others whose hands bore the ingrained soil of the fields of Judea. In the churches that Paul established during our travels we'd got used to congregations that cut right across any kind of local class structure. So I was pleased to see that social status didn't seem to matter much now to the Jewish Christians either.

(When I remarked on this to someone later, I was told that things had previously been very different. James had felt it necessary to set down in writing some very firm instructions on the absolute need for Followers of the Way to be inclusive and fair, castigating some of the wealthy believers for behaving as if they were a superior species. Copies of this document had been distributed widely through the provinces, as it also contained a lot of practical advice as well as encouragement for Jews who'd become followers of Jesus. However, I kept to myself the observation that the traditional exclusion of women from religious leadership evidently persisted in Jerusalem. Knowing the calibre of some of the women already holding positions of responsibility in churches elsewhere in the empire, I thought this was a pity, but realised that such a major cultural shift might take a long time to come about.)

Paul took his seat a few places to my right with Simon Peter and a serious-looking man in his mid-forties I assumed to be James. I spotted Barnabas with Titus and John Mark in the back row, away to my left, and gave them a surreptitious wave.

James (for it was indeed he) got to his feet, and the buzz of conversation subsided. "Brothers," he said, "you all know why we're here today. Let us begin by asking our Lord to give us wisdom and understanding by his Holy Spirit, so that what we decide will be in accordance with his divine will." Then he prayed a short prayer in the same manner as he might have spoken to a close friend or family member – which, I suppose, was the case. After that he set out some ground rules for the debate, saying, "I know that there are very strong feelings about the matter before us today, and that words have been already spoken that would have been far better unsaid. Therefore, keep this in mind, that we are brothers in our faith. Let every man listen with open ears and open heart. Think before you speak, and do not let your emotions get the better of your tongue. If we want to discern what is right in our Lord's eyes, we must not let personal opinions get in the way! We all know that the enemy would love to see the church divided."

Once started, the discussions went on at great length, in Aramaic rather than the more familiar Greek. Fortunately, my ear was fairly well tuned to the language by now, so I could follow the discussion easily enough. Anyone who felt that he had a valid contribution was allowed to take the floor, and as feelings ran deep and strong on both sides, the debate did become pretty heated at times. Paul and Barnabas, however, remained silent and in their seats.

It was well after midday when Simon Peter gave his conclusion, along these lines: "Gentlemen, my brothers in Christ, you are well aware of the fact that it was the Lord himself who in a vision made it clear to me that we should share his message also with those outside our Jewish faith. And you know that the Lord seems just as willing to give his Holy Spirit to them as to us. That means his invitation to them is a genuine offer of free salvation. Why then do you now want to risk trying our Lord's patience by imposing on these new believers a legalistic burden which neither our ancestors nor we today were able to bear? Surely the crucial fact is that it is by the grace of our Lord Jesus that we are saved, through faith – just as they are. Where's the argument with that?"

There was not a single word of dissent. James now invited Paul and Barnabas to describe in detail all that the Lord had done through them on their travels. With the rapt attention of everyone in the room, they took turns to address their audience. As I heard them talk about the miraculous healings, meetings that seemed to have been divinely appointed, protection from enemies, forming of deep friendships, and above all the establishment of thriving churches full of men and women living in the joy and power of the Holy Spirit, memories flooded back and I longed to be out on the mission road again.

At last, silence fell once more. All eyes were on James, who took his seat to give his adjudication. It didn't take long. In essence, his considered view was that it was entirely in line with words of the prophets of old that the Lord God would at some point include those outside the Jewish nation to be among His chosen people. All those present had heard detailed evidence from Paul and the others that this must now be the case. Therefore, they should not place any obstacles before non-Jews who were now turning towards the Lord – just a few sensible instructions on what was deemed acceptable behaviour, so as not to cause offence to their Jewish neighbours.

Following a further short discussion, there was complete agreement that representatives of the Jerusalem church should go back to Antioch with us to vouch for the accuracy of our report. They selected Judas Barsabbas, and Silvanus (known to all as Silas), who both held respected positions of leadership in the church.

At this point, I was called forward to take down a letter in my best Greek. This is how it went:

"From the apostles and elders in Jerusalem, your brothers in the Lord Jesus, greetings to those of you who are non-Jews in the church in Antioch, and in the provinces of Syria and Cilicia in general. Having heard of your deep distress and confusion, after you'd received certain teaching that, we assure you, did not originate with us, we have agreed to send trustworthy representatives back to you with Paul and Barnabas. Therefore, we are sending you Judas and Silas, men who have risked their lives for the name of the Lord Jesus Christ, and who will in their own words ratify the content of this letter.

"Having listened to the Holy Spirit and to our own consciences, we feel it is right that no extra burden should be placed upon you than the following simple requirements: avoid any activities involving idols; respect the dietary beliefs of your Jewish fellow-Christians, with regard to blood, for instance; shun sexual immorality. If you adhere to this sensible code of conduct, we see no reason why there should be any further issue between us.

"May the Lord be with you all!"

Although some of the former Pharisees were still rather uneasy about this, the conference ended on a generally positive note with a closing prayer and blessing from James. He left promptly with some of the other elders, and I was disappointed not to get to speak to him.

Our departure from Jerusalem was (fortunately) delayed by a spell of unusually severe weather, rain storms causing flooding on many roads in the district. This gave me the chance to have a close look at the Temple – well, as close as a non-Jew is permitted to get – when I discovered that it's almost a city within the City, with its own thriving business set-up, as well as all the religious activities. I've been told how during his final visit there, Jesus had shown uncharacteristic anger in the Temple precincts, overturning the tables of money-changers and people selling animals and birds for sacrifice, shouting out, "It is written in the scriptures, 'My house shall be called a house of prayer' – but you have made it a den of thieves!" Some who witnessed the event said that it was almost as if Jesus was trying to provoke the authorities to arrest him. (The Roman garrison has from the start been sited close to the Temple, as it's recognised as the most likely place for trouble to flare up, and there have been several attempted rebellions in recent years.)

Later, I took the opportunity to talk to some of the other people who'd known Jesus personally, both before and after his resurrection. This was achieved partly through John Mark, who seemed to know everybody. It struck me that he had matured a lot in the couple of years since he'd abandoned his travels with us at Perga. I enjoyed a delicious meal at his mother's house, which had been a frequent meeting-place for Jesus and his friends, and where I heard first-hand accounts of some of the teachings of Jesus.

One special meeting Mark arranged for me was with Mary, Jesus' mother. Although now in her mid-sixties, she possessed an extraordinary aura of grace and peace that made her somehow ageless. After Jesus had been crucified she had become adopted mother to another John, who'd become a follower of Jesus in the very early days in Galilee. Mary and I chatted for a very long while, although our meeting seemed to come to an end all too soon. Later, I was also able to speak to John himself, who combined a cheerful, boyish demeanour with great wisdom and spiritual insight. Like Peter, he'd been brought up as a fisherman on Lake Tiberias, but you'd never guess that now, apart from the occasional tinge of dialect in his speech.

There were others I met too, and all of them were more than happy to tell me in detail about Jesus and the effect he'd had on their lives. Many had been convinced that Jesus was about to re-establish the kingdom of Israel, driving out the Romans in the process, and they were left totally distraught when that didn't happen. It took a long time for them to understand that Jesus had indeed established a new kingdom, but quite unlike any earthly one. They evidently still found it hard to put into words all the mixed emotions they'd experienced when meeting him again alive, after they'd seen him dead and buried. (Thanks to these conversations, I gleaned a lot more material for my book.) Paul, meanwhile, was surprised and delighted to get a visit from his nephew, Jonathan, having not even known that he was in Jerusalem. He seemed a very pleasant, thoughtful youth, who had originally planned to train as a Pharisee like his uncle, but was now himself a believer in Jesus.

A few days later we were heading home, our party slightly enlarged by the presence of John Mark, who'd evidently regained his desire to travel. He and Titus seemed to have a lot in common. Once back in Antioch, we got word out to our fellow Christians there, so there was soon a very excited crowd of people, keen to receive the report from Jerusalem. They found the contents of the letter very encouraging, and there was quite a party. Silas and Judas were both inspirational preachers, and spent some weeks with us in Antioch, giving many talks and helping to build up the faith and understanding of the believers.

It wasn't long after this that Paul suggested to Barnabas that it would be good to go back and visit all the places in the provinces where they had proclaimed the message of the kingdom. He was anxious to find out how the churches were getting on.

Barnabas said, "Yes, of course. Great idea! We can take John Mark with us."

Paul responded most angrily to this suggestion. "Absolutely not! After the way that boy deserted us before? He's not made of the right stuff, and I refuse to let him come!"

Sad to relate, this episode caused such a deep rift between Barnabas and Paul that they totally fell out. We were all very upset about it, and while it was difficult not to take sides, I couldn't help recalling what James had said in Jerusalem about not letting our emotions have free reign with our tongue. Still in a major huff, Barnabas fairly soon closed the matter by saying, "Well, I'm getting too old for all this travelling around, anyway," took Mark, and sailed back home to Cyprus. We assumed that we'd never see either of them again.

It's fair to say that Paul was devastated by this turn of events – he blamed himself for the destruction of a precious friendship. It was difficult to know what to say to him. But there were absolutely no recriminations from the other church leaders, and once Paul had calmed down enough they all spent several days in fasting, prayer and discussion. The outcome of this was the decision by Silas not to return to Jerusalem, but instead to join Paul's team for the next mission. Shortly after that I was once more instructed to pack my bags and prepare for a journey.

Travel Diaries – Series II

September 21[18]

There are five of us being sent out with the blessing of the Antioch church: Paul, Silas, Alexander, Titus and me. Paul says that Titus, though young, is full of potential and will one day be a leader. It has been agreed that we shall take the overland route, as it's so late in the year that the prospect of storms at sea makes travelling by ship decidedly unappealing, if not hazardous. Our initial goal is Paul's home town, Tarsus, which we should reach within five days. Alexander's brother-in-law has lent us a donkey and cart for this first leg of our journey, so I'm pleased that I shan't be carrying all my baggage the whole way.

September 29

Arrived in Tarsus. Slight delay on the journey as, in one town just north of Antioch, we found a group of Christians who seem to have got some rather muddled ideas about what the Good News really is. Some of them had not even been baptized. Paul and Silas sat them all down and went through a basic course of instruction, explaining that while their personal salvation was entirely based upon believing wholeheartedly in Jesus as the Anointed One sent by God to set the world to rights, there also needed to be visible evidence of a willingness to be changed from the inside. There was a late-night party afterwards, people having been baptized and receiving the gifts of the Holy Spirit.

---

[18] 49 AD

September 30

We're enjoying first-class hospitality from Paul's sister Judith and her husband Benjamin. You'd never guess she was even related to Paul, being unusually tall with a mass of dark brown curls – takes after their father, it seems. They're delighted to get news of their son Jonathan in Jerusalem, having heard nothing from him for nearly a year. They've described to us how, as strict Jews, they had at first been reluctant to receive the Good News of the kingdom when Saul (as they still call him) returned to Tarsus in the early days. However, the way he had changed as a person, as well as his expert teaching from the scriptures, convinced them that what he was claiming had to be true. Judith and, to a lesser extent, Benjamin are now leaders in a growing church in the city, and held in high regard for the work they are doing with the poor.

October 2

Paul has been busy today, negotiating the sale of some family property to release funds to help us on our travels. Once that transaction is complete, we'll be heading off for Derbe. I've enjoyed a few days' rest, but am now really looking forward to meeting the friends I made there on our first journey. Titus and I went to the market and got a good supply of dried dates at a reasonable price. They make a very tasty snack when you're on the road.

October 5

The going underfoot may be smooth, but progress is quite slow as we climb into the mountains, and I seem to need to rest more often than I used to. It does give me a chance to sit and appreciate the view, mountain-tops dusted with snow in one direction, and the shimmering sea stretching into invisibility in the other. Paul is impatient to be back among friends in Derbe, and keeps on saying out loud things like, "I wonder how so-and-so has been getting on…" He seems unable to keep people out of his thoughts, and it's quite normal to hear him suddenly praying to the Lord on someone's behalf as we're walking along. He really loves them.

October 7

Today we passed through the famed Cilician Gates, where the highway runs through a steep-sided gash in the mountains, little more than twenty paces wide in parts. Even though I came through quite unscathed on my journey back from our first trip to Galatia, I couldn't help feeling then and now that it's an excellent place for being ambushed. Alexander sensibly pointed out that the route is too well-used by the military for bandits to be much of a threat. We have seen several squads of soldiers out on exercise since we left Tarsus, as well as parties of traders.

October 10

We're now on the high plateau once more and making better progress. The air is chilly, but conditions are calm, with the outlines of distant peaks sharp against the sky. Last night we were glad of the log fire in the lodging-house where we stayed. Talking to people there, Paul was delighted to learn that the Good News about Jesus is spreading (even without his involvement), and someone has suggested he should visit a small town some miles off our route, to encourage the group of believers there. It looks as though we'll be taking a detour which will delay us a bit, but Paul seems quite happy with that prospect.

October 13

I can't either pronounce or spell the name of the town we're in now, as it's in the Lycaonian language and, as we found before, even having a conversation is difficult. The news about Jesus reached here from Derbe quite soon after our first visit, and there is a small but active church. They are eager to hear things from Paul's own lips, but he has to speak through an interpreter, which slows things down and makes it very difficult to get some ideas across.

The people here are very welcoming, if a bit uncultured. As in many other places where the Good News has been preached, it seems the new Christians have had a real impact on their local community, living as though the Lord Jesus himself is here with them. We've been told of a long-standing family blood feud that has been resolved, and there's no end of stories of people being healed from both physical and mental illnesses. Paul finds it all very rewarding and reassuring, compensating for those times when his teaching seems to have fallen on deaf ears and hearts of stone.

October 23

After a couple more minor detours, we're at last in Derbe. They must have had advance warning of our approach, as there was a cheering crowd waiting to greet us at the city gate. There was a lot of back-slapping between Paul and Gaius, while Silas, Titus and Alexander had to be personally introduced to all and sundry. When asked about Barnabas, Paul simply said that he'd had to go back to Cyprus. Recalling what had happened with him still makes me feel very sad.

October 25

Everyone got together this evening to share in the celebration meal that we now simply call the "Lord's Supper", so the meeting-house was packed with excited people. Gaius has really grown in faith, flourishing in his role as leader of the church here. Already, some of the young men of Derbe are being trained up to go and take the Good News of the kingdom to other parts of the empire, and the believers seem to have a solid faith and strong sense of community. I think that this has been a pleasant surprise to Paul, and he's said that we don't need to stay here very long. He does, however, want to spend some time with Gaius and the other local church leaders before we leave.

October 30

We arrived in Lystra last evening, and are staying once more at the home of dear Lois. Already well into her seventies, she has been unwell for some months, but was overjoyed to see us again. I'm hoping that some of my treatments will help her. Timothy, her grandson, now twenty years of age, has impressed the leaders of the church here with his maturity, wisdom and zeal for sharing the Good News. This evening Paul said to me, "I'm really fond of him, you know. I'd like him to join us on our travels. Trouble is, Eunice his mother was widowed during last winter, so there might be issues over Timothy's assumed role as man of the house. We must pray to the Lord about it."

November 1

Today being the Lord's Day, we joined our brothers and sisters here for the Lord's Supper. Silas read out to everyone the letter from the church leaders in Jerusalem, with the recommendations that were agreed at the conference there. Most people have been delighted at what they've heard, although some of the Jewish believers feel that not requiring a man to be circumcised is pushing things a bit too far in the direction of compromise. This puts Timothy in a very awkward position, if he is to be given a responsible position in the church here.

November 4

Following some lengthy discussions, Timothy has agreed to undergo the circumcision ceremony, in spite of it not being a formal requirement in becoming a Christian. Paul is anxious not to create obstacles to the faith of some very pious Jews in the Christian community here, nor provide a cause for division in the local church. All credit to Timothy, in that he didn't seem to mind either way!

November 11

Everything has been sorted out with Timothy's family, and he is after all going to join us as we travel on, first to Iconium and then once more to Antioch in Galatia province. Paul is starting to treat Timothy like the son he never had, to the extent that Silas joked that he was "going soft". I don't see any change in Paul's steely resolve to take the Good News as far as he can across the empire, including to Rome itself. That'll be a challenge, as we heard not long ago that Claudius Caesar has issued an edict expelling Jews from the city.

November 13

On the road again, our party having now grown to six. Timothy is no longer feeling sore after his circumcision, and is more than willing to carry a share of the baggage. Happily, we have much kinder weather than the snowstorms that we endured on our first visit to the region. I hadn't previously noticed the fine twelve-arched bridge that carries the road across one of the rivers. There would have been a long detour without it, as the valley bottom looked very marshy.

Life settled back into the familiar routine, as we made our way slowly north-west across the province of Galatia, visiting the growing number of churches in the region. I spent some time getting to know Timothy, who seemed to hold Paul in a position of awe. I said, "Look at him as your role-model, but don't fear him. Don't you realise just how fond he is of you? I think he sees you as a future leader." The weather remained cold but dry, so travelling was comparatively easy. We faced very little opposition, rather being continually surprised by the hospitality and generosity of the people we met, even in Antioch. The content of the letter from the elders in Jerusalem was always received very enthusiastically, and most non-Jewish believers naturally found it really encouraging.

There was a noticeable absence of any sense of "them and us" in most of the Christian gatherings, gratifying to observe. Silas and Paul, as always, spent a lot of time teaching about how the Jewish scriptures demonstrate that Jesus of Nazareth is the promised Redeemer of the whole world (not just the Jews). His resurrection has changed the course of history. And they kept emphasising his imminent return: "Don't put off your decision! Time is running out, if you want to be ready to meet him when he comes!" Every day there were new believers asking to be baptized in Jesus' name, and receiving the Holy Spirit. Routine, maybe – but far from dull!

December 30

This morning, glad of the sunshine warming our backs, we headed west on the main road from Antioch with the intention of crossing into the province of Asia[19]. After some miles, Alexander told Paul and Silas that something was troubling him. All he could say was that he felt convinced that we were going the wrong way. We stopped for a while by Milestone IX, and prayed to the Lord for some instructions. In due course, Silas said that he felt that the Lord was indeed telling us we were not to go to Asia – at least, not yet. So we've returned to Antioch.

---

[19] western Turkey

Very frustrating, but at least we hadn't gone too far to get back before dark.

January 1[20]

Paul and Silas have decided that we should take the north road from Antioch in the direction of Bithynia and Pontus on the shores of the Euxine Sea[21]. We know that the Good News was taken there by people who witnessed the events at that famous Feast of Pentecost in Jerusalem. Paul is keen to visit any churches that may have grown up over the years, to make sure they have a proper grounding in the faith.

January 9

This morning some travellers we met warned us of armed bandits on the road ahead – they'd had a narrow escape themselves, they said. Again, we have sensed the Spirit of the Lord forbidding us to go on any farther north, much to Paul's disappointment. Instead, we have turned westward to cross the northern fringe of Asia, through well-wooded countryside that allows a glimpse from time to time of the sea far away on our right-hand side. This road is little more than a track, with every now and then a small village. At least the ground is fairly level and the weather dry, so we're making good progress.

January 10

Last night we slept in our cloaks huddled around the embers of the fire. It was bitterly cold, and we were glad that there was no wind. Food's getting a bit short, too. Timothy seems to be putting up very well with the rigours of being on the road, and never complains. I think that it's good for him that we have Titus with us – young enough to relate to him, but with much more experience. Most of the local people we've encountered speak their own dialect, and are not very fluent in Greek. While not being actually hostile to us, they haven't shown us much hospitality either. It also means that Paul finds it difficult to share the message, so he is urging us to press on as fast as we can towards the west coast. There are several important towns in Asia that we hope to

---

[20] 50 AD
[21] Black Sea

then be able to reach by sea; we have no way of knowing how widely the Good News has yet been spread in that region.

January 15

At last we've reached the port of Troas, very rich and very Roman, in the north-west corner of Asia province. The weather is noticeably warmer down here by the sea, which is a blessing. There is a busy market with traders from all over the empire, so we've been able to stock up with much-needed supplies. We'd not enjoyed a square meal for three days. The Roman administration has evidently invested a lot of money in developments here in recent years, and we've really appreciated the baths, after several days freezing in the backwoods. Alexander and I are staying in a small lodging house near the quay, with instructions to find a ship that can take us south along the coast towards Ephesus. The others are in lodgings in the higher part of the town where there is a small Jewish community, and Paul and Silas hope to speak in the synagogue on the coming Sabbath.

January 16

A significant change of plan! Rather than heading south, it seems we need to find a vessel that will take us west to Macedonia province. When we met the others this morning, we could sense some excitement. Paul explained that he'd been woken by a vivid dream in the night, in which a Macedonian man was standing on the far shore, calling out, "Come over here to Macedonia! Help us, please!" He's convinced that this is a clear message from the Lord, and wants us to set sail as soon as possible. Ephesus can wait, it seems.

January 17

Westbound ships sail almost every day, calling at Neapolis, so we have arranged to set off tomorrow on a small trading vessel, which will stop overnight at Samothrace[22], about the halfway point on our journey. The weather is set fair, with a following wind, so we don't expect any problems this time. I'm quite sorry not to be staying longer in Troas, as

---

[22] Samothraki

it's a lively place full of interesting people. Still, I expect we'll come back this way in due course.

January 18

Samothrace: I'm amazed that anyone would want to live here! As we approached, the island slowly grew on the horizon as a cloud-capped mountain emerging from the sea. It is all very rugged and has no harbour, so our ship is at anchor in a wide bay on the north side of the island, and we've been ferried ashore in small, brightly painted boats that came out to greet us. The Samothracians seem a very friendly people – perhaps because they depend a lot on the travellers, who give them their main source of income, along with fishing. They are also famously independent, and the island has not even been annexed by Rome. Well, not growing corn nor supplying metal ores, it's probably not worth the effort… But they do have a surprisingly large temple to "The Great Gods", whoever they might be!

January 19

After some excellent hospitality and a good night's sleep, we set sail soon after dawn. It is now about noon and the snow-capped mountains of Macedonia are clearly visible against a pale blue sky ahead of us. Silas and Paul have been getting on well with the ship's captain, chatting about what should be the next stage of our journey, once we've set foot in Europe. "Head for Philippi," is his advice. It's only half a day's journey inland on the Egnatian Way, and by far the most important city in the region. I understand that, as in the case of Troas, it was designated a "colonia" by Caesar Augustus himself, many years ago. With a fair-sized Roman element in the population, it is now governed by two officials appointed directly from Rome. For some reason, Paul feels that this might play out in our favour.

January 20

Reasonable accommodation last night, in one of the many hostelries down by the harbour. Businesses in Neapolis rely heavily on through-traffic, it would appear. We breakfasted before dawn, in order to make an early start. Although the road is built to a very high standard, our progress is rather slow, as it seems to be uphill all the way. We're roughly halfway now, at Milestone VIII, and all glad of a chance for some rest and refreshment at a wayside hostelry. Paul is carrying out repairs to Timothy's left sandal. He'll probably need new footwear before long. I've lost track of how many pairs of shoes I've worn out in the last few years...

January 21

Philippi is impressive, even by the standards that we've come across in some of the other great cities on our travels. It was founded by the great king Philip of Macedonia more than three hundred years ago, with exceptionally fine architecture, paid for with gold mined in the mountains north of here. Now very much under the influence of Rome, with citizenship being a privilege bestowed on everyone born here, there's a new forum under construction, and the enlarged theatre is now claimed to be one of the grandest in the whole empire. The only thing missing is a synagogue – we've gathered that the Jewish community is very small, and seems to run along informal lines. We're told that on the Sabbath Day they gather for a meeting at a certain spot down by the Gangites River, just off the main road out of the city.

It's still rather chilly, and I'm not used to the sun being so low in the sky at noon. They say it gets worse, the farther you go into Europe. I'm concerned about Alexander, as he doesn't seem to be very well – quite lethargic. Not at all like him.

January 22

Alexander has a fever. I stayed with him at our lodgings this morning when the others went off to find out more about what's going on in the city. I mixed my patient a potion which seemed to calm him down, and he had some sleep. This afternoon I was able to visit an apothecary and restock some of my medicines. The man was quite interested in the idea of me being an itinerant physician, although I tried to explain the real reason for my travels.

January 23

It was just as we'd heard. Today being the Sabbath, we went to the meeting place described, where we found a gathering of about twenty women, Jews and God-fearing Greeks. No men – unusual. Paul's teaching, as he explained to them the Good News of the kingdom, really grabbed the interest of some of them, none more so than a distinguished lady named Lydia. Talking to her, we've found out that she's a businesswoman from Thyatira, back in Asia province. Her trade is in purple cloth, so she has some very important clients (not mentioning any names!) She's got a home here in Philippi too, for when she's visiting to oversee the purchase of new supplies of dye imported from Tyre. As well as being very rich, and clearly a person of some influence in the city, she is a believer in God and has willingly received Paul's message about the Messiah being Jesus.

January 24

Lydia wastes no time. She's shared the Good News with her whole household, and Paul and Silas baptized eleven of them today in the river, at the meeting place. Lydia has opened her home to us for as long as we need to stay, saying, "If you're satisfied that I'm genuinely a believer in Jesus as Lord, then do me the honour of staying at my house." And she's not the kind of person that takes no for an answer...

January 27

We are being very well looked after in our new lodgings, and Alexander is benefiting from being in a more comfortable bed. It seems that Lydia is an accomplished society hostess, and very well known in the city's business community. Already, we have a daily routine that sees us go down to the riverside meeting place, where growing numbers of people have been coming to hear what Silas, Paul and the others have to say. There's been an increased level of curiosity today, as a young slave girl followed us down there, shouting out, "These men are working for the God Most High! They have a message for you – how to find salvation!" It seems she has this knowledge thanks to a spirit of clairvoyance, and her owners apparently make a lot of profit from her ability to foretell the future.

February 5

The daily performance by the slave girl has started to attract the wrong sort of attention, and today Paul had had enough. He stopped in his tracks, turned around, and addressing the demon spirit in the girl, shouted, "In the name of Jesus the Messiah, I command you to come out of her – now!" Instantly, the poor girl screamed and fell to the ground writhing, before starting to laugh and cry at the same time. After a few minutes of this, she lay back with the most beautiful, serene smile on her face, evidently free of possession and in her right mind.

This episode caused a near riot, with the slave girl's owners realising that their business had been ruined, and Paul and Silas were now in serious trouble. With the rest of us following at a safe distance, the two of them were dragged back into the city, to the forum, and set before the Roman magistrates there with the accusation, "These Jews are creating a disturbance in our city! They're bringing false teaching in order to undermine Roman law and order. We're not putting up with it any longer!"

We could only look on helplessly, as punishment was administered there and then. Silas and Paul were publicly stripped and beaten unconscious with rods by the magistrates' officers, and then taken away. We don't know where. This is certainly the worst thing that has happened in our travels so far, and all of us in Lydia's currently extended household have been praying to the Lord that they will be safe.

February 6

So much to tell! Desperately worried over Silas and Paul, none of us got much sleep last night, and things were made worse by a violent earthquake that struck about midnight. Everybody got out of the house as quickly as possible, but apart from some ornaments falling off a shelf and breaking, there was no damage and no one was hurt. After that, nobody felt like sleeping anyway, and we sat around talking and praying, and waiting for the day. Then, having breakfasted, we decided that it would be wise not to go to the meeting place today. We simply didn't know what to do.

Mid-morning we were all amazed and delighted when one of Lydia's maids, Eudora, shouted out, "Here they are! It's Paul and Silas! They're back!" We all rushed to meet them in the hallway, full of questions about what had happened to them.

Paul waved his hands to quieten us down, and then said, "Just listen to this, everyone! Hear how our Lord Jesus gets the job done! Yesterday evening Silas and I found ourselves chained up in jail, like convicts. We refused to believe that the Lord would abandon us there, so we prayed and sang hymns – the other prisoners thought we were mad. Then, about midnight – that earthquake! You must have felt it! The prison shook to its foundations, the doors all flew open and everyone's chains fell off. The jailer came rushing in, expecting to find everyone gone, and drew his sword to kill himself rather than answer to the magistrates for his failings. 'It's alright!' I shouted in the darkness. 'We're all here.'

"The jailer, in total panic and shaking all over, called for lights and came and led us out of our cell. Clutching us by the arms, he begged us, 'Sirs, you can see I'm up to my neck in trouble now! How can I save my skin?' I don't know what answer he was expecting, but we shared the Good News of the Lord Jesus with him. He found it all quite astonishing, and then wanted everyone in his household to hear it as well. In next to no time, we found ourselves in his house with our wounds washed and a meal set before us, as we told our story all over again. The happy result of that is that our erstwhile jailer, Theron, and all his family have now been baptized into the kingdom. It's wonderful!

"That's not the end of it. Early this morning, Theron came and told us that city officials had turned up with a message from the magistrates, to the effect that we should be released and permitted to go on our way in peace. 'I'm not having that!' I thought. I went out to speak to them myself. 'You know what has been done to us,' I said. 'We've been beaten within an inch of our lives, and then thrown into prison – in spite of the fact that we're both Roman citizens! Now they just want us to leave quietly? No way! Tell them they're to come to us, here and now!'

"We didn't have to wait very long. I think the magistrates are fearful for their own future, if word gets out about the serious breach of protocol they've perpetrated. They couldn't have been more apologetic, and led us out from the prison themselves. They've politely requested that we leave the city, which we shall be doing – but not just yet. The main thing was to come back to you all and encourage you in your faith."

An exciting day, today. What more can I say?

February 8

With Lydia and her friend Euodia very willing to take responsibility for the group of believers who now meet regularly in her house, we feel that it is time to move on. Although we've been here less than three weeks, we've made many close friendships in the city, and I can tell that Paul has a genuine fondness for the little church here.

February 9

A day for tying up loose ends, and packing up in preparation for the next stage in our journey. We all shared the Lord's Supper together this evening, with not a few tears being shed on both sides. Paul was especially moved by a very generous gift of money from the church, to help fund our continuing mission to spread the Good News.

February 10

We're heading west on the Egnatian Way, now about halfway to Thessalonica[23], having bypassed Amphipolis ("None of my brothers there!" said Paul) but stopping for the night at a comfortable inn on the outskirts of Apollonia. The road is always very busy, so there is accommodation of some kind or another at regular intervals, although some of the premises don't look very inviting. Having made good progress today, we decided to stop off quite early before everywhere got full. Our group has changed slightly, Alexander having decided to return home following his illness, so he should be sailing from Neapolis within the next day or so. However, from the church in Philippi we've been joined by Urbanus and Rufus, on their way back to Rome and keen to share the Good News there. Paul's stated purpose remains to get there in person one day.

February 12

First impressions of Thessalonica are that it's more Greek than Roman. On the main highway and with its own port, the city (much bigger than I imagined) is busy and has grown wealthy through trade. It has to be said that this is largely thanks to the thriving Jewish community, which is concentrated in the lower quarter near the harbour. In contrast to Philippi, there is a large synagogue here, and Silas and Paul have already met the leaders. They hope to be able to speak there on the coming Sabbath.

---

[23] in northern Greece

February 15

In the last few days I've really noticed how the noonday sun is getting higher in the sky, and the air is feeling much warmer now. A beautiful morning, and Paul and Silas went off early to the synagogue. Urbanus has been showing Titus, Timothy and me the main attractions of the city, which he's visited several times before. He took us to visit some Roman friends of his, who were delighted to meet us. Over a most enjoyable lunch, we talked to them about Jesus and the Good News of his kingdom. All in all, a very pleasant way to spend a day off.

February 18

A surprise visit from two of Lydia's household staff today. They'd been specially commissioned to bring another large donation of money from Philippi. It seems that quite a few people missed out on the opportunity to contribute before we left the city, but really wanted to do so. Rarely have we encountered that level of generosity. It's really very encouraging for us all.

February 23

After promising signs last week, when Paul and Silas were well received at the synagogue, it sounds as though resistance to the Good News is growing – among the Jews at least. As is his usual practice, Paul has been reasoning from the scriptures to show that what he's saying has to be true, but this has often resulted in heated arguments, and that doesn't always bring out the best in him. However, many non-Jews have received the message gladly, including some of the influential women of the city, which is probably making things worse.

March 2

Things came to a head yesterday. It was the third Sabbath in a row that Silas and Paul had spent time at the synagogue, employing their finest reasoning in trying to convince the Jews. This time they were interrupted, as the leaders there had arranged for some rabble-rousers to turn up and create a disturbance.

Silas and Paul had to be smuggled out and hidden in someone's home not far away, for their own safety. The mob went to the house of

Jason, one of the new believers living nearby, thinking they were there, and failing to find them, angrily took Jason, Urbanus and a couple of the others off to the city authorities. The accusation levelled by the Jews was along the lines of, "These men who've been turning the world upside down have now come here to do the same thing! They're openly speaking treachery against Caesar by claiming there is some other king called Jesus who's really the one in charge – and Jason here is sheltering them somewhere, so he's as bad as the rest!" This got everybody really alarmed, and Jason and the others were only released after agreeing to be bound over to keep the peace.

It's now after midnight, and we've all managed to get reunited in a safe-house, but are in the process of packing up our stuff in order to leave the city under cover of darkness. Paul would have liked to spend more time instructing the new believers here, but it's clearly no longer sensible for us to be here.

March 4

We've walked until we can scarcely place one foot in front of the other, putting as much distance as possible between Thessalonica and ourselves. Fortunately, it's a good road across the plain, and we're feeling a lot safer now. Mount Olympus and its snow-capped peaks are looming ever larger away to the south.

March 5

Arrived at Beroea: in the foothills of Mount Olympus, and slightly off the Egnatian Way. Seems a much quieter place than Thessalonica, and we've been well received at the Jewish synagogue.

There was a highly improbable coincidence this evening. We were talking with other guests at the inn where we're staying, and I mentioned that my home is Antioch in Syria, at which a very wizened old man across the table cried out, "Oh, do you know Anaxagoras of Athens?" This enquiry led to a long and rather excited conversation, although I had the sad duty of telling Archippus, my new friend, that Anaxagoras had died some years ago. The two of them had studied together in Athens many years back, but had lost touch when my former master's business interests caused him to move to Syria.

March 7

We have never before had such an encouraging response to the Good News. The Jews here in Beroea have mostly accepted it eagerly, studying the scriptures assiduously themselves to ensure that what Paul and Silas have been teaching really stands up to scrutiny. Many non-Jews are also becoming believers, particularly (as in Thessalonica) women from the higher echelons of society. That's interesting... As a non-Jew himself, Titus is becoming a very effective teacher in his own right. We've been offered an unusual level of hospitality, with more gifts of money too, to help our mission.

March 21

Today we've had to split up. After things had been going so well, we were woken very early this morning. Pyrrhus's son Sopater and one of the others came with news that a gang has been here, sent by the Jews in Thessalonica. Evidently, they've heard that the Beroeans are receiving the teaching about Jesus and want to put a stop to it by causing trouble in the city. Some of the brothers from the church are escorting us – that is, Paul, Timothy, Rufus and me – down to the coast. We hope to find a vessel that will take us south to Athens, in Achaia province. Silas, Titus and the others will be keeping a low profile in Beroea for a while, but Paul has left instructions for them to join us as soon as possible.

Later: I realise now that I've left my spare cloak behind, but at least the weather is much warmer now. For the first time in months, I reckon that we've enjoyed a full twelve hours of daylight today.

March 23

We're Athens-bound, sharing a small cargo ship with some goats, not the most peaceful of travelling companions... The journey will take some days, as we have to call at a number of minor ports on the way, but at least we're safe here. We're keeping fairly close to the coast, which is rugged with many promontories and small islands, and quite difficult to navigate, I imagine. The crew seems to be very experienced, well aware of the potential hazards, and full of cheerful banter.

March 27

A strong wind from the north-east has forced our ship to take shelter, but since there is a good road to Athens only a short distance inland, we've been advised to continue our journey on foot. It'll be quicker too, we're told. After being rather cooped up on the ship, we're all in need of some proper exercise now. We all smell strongly of goat, as well, and are looking forward to a bath and change of clothing.

April 1

Within sight of Athens, we're spending tonight at a roadside inn where we can get cleaned up before entering the city tomorrow. We wouldn't want to be mistaken for a bunch of tramps! One thing we've gathered about the Athenians is that they like everything to be "just so". I wonder what Paul will think of the place...

April 2

No visitor to Athens can fail to be impressed by the grandeur of the city, with its sixty-foot-high walls, and streets neatly laid out in a rectangular pattern centred on the "agora" or city-centre square. There are buildings as magnificent as any I've yet seen anywhere, but many walls bear notices (beautifully carved in marble) giving detailed rules and instructions from the civic authorities on just about every aspect of life in the city. They seem to love uniformity of behaviour here. Above everything towers the great Temple of Athena, an astonishing blend of art and architecture. There are temples to many other gods too, and every indication that the place is a focus for the worship of idols. It's also a centre of learning with a number of famous Schools of Philosophy. The intellectuals here apparently seize every new idea that arises and debate it into the dust, so to speak. I think that we're in for a bit of challenge.

April 7

Silas and Titus have still not turned up, and we're all at a bit of a loose end. Paul is still grieving over having to abandon the believers in Thessalonica before he'd finished what he planned to do there. He's writing a short letter of encouragement which he's asked Timothy to take to them. With the weather very favourable for sailing now, the sea journey from Piraeus shouldn't take him more than three days. I did some more sightseeing in the city, and had no difficulty tracking down some relatives of Anaxagoras – very wealthy people – but they weren't very welcoming to me, once I revealed that I was their cousin's former slave. This was disappointing, especially in view of the reputation of Athens as a promoter of social equality among its citizens.

As the Jewish community here is quite small and lacking influence, the level of blatant idolatry in the city has become very exasperating to Paul. He's had several serious discussions about this in the synagogue, and also in the agora where he's quite prepared to tackle some of the philosophers head-on. The general stress of the situation has been causing his digestion to misbehave, which in turn makes him more short-tempered than normal. I'm doing my best on his behalf.

April 9

There was a significant development today. Rufus and I were with Paul in the city centre this morning, in our role as observers, more than anything else, as neither of us is skilled in philosophical debate. A group of intellectuals were attracted by what Paul was saying, as they evidently thought he was proclaiming two new foreign gods, called "Jesus" and "Resurrection". This of course got them excited, and they took him off to the Mars Hill Council, which seems to function as the city's Board of Intellectual Scrutiny. Rufus and I were able to follow them, and we squeezed into the public gallery to see what might ensue.

Rarely have I witnessed Paul be more eloquent. The President of the Council said to him, "Tell us, please – what is this teaching that you're spreading around? It all sounds very strange to our ears, and we'd like an explanation." Considering the degree to which Paul has been growing in his dislike for the city, he excelled himself in his politeness, tact and wisdom.

Commending the "Gentlemen of Athens" for their religious zeal, he said that on his way he had noticed an altar dedicated to The God Whom No One Knows. "That God," he declared, "whom you worship in ignorance, is the one whom I'm here to proclaim! He's the Lord of both heaven and earth, he doesn't need a temple made by human hands – in fact, he doesn't need anything, because it's from him that we humans have life and breath and everything else we need."

Paul then continued for some time, referring to their own poets and philosophers, to show how this God desired all mankind to seek him, and to see themselves as his beloved children. "Your times of ignorance he will overlook," he said, "but now you need to change the way you think and the way you live, because Judgment Day is coming. He will measure each person against the standard set by the man who is perfect, appointed by him – and he has guaranteed this to be so by raising that man from the dead!"

That really threw the cat among the pigeons. Many of those listening fell about laughing at the idea of anyone being raised from the dead, although there were a few who said that they wanted to hear more on the subject. Paul chose not to enter into any further discussions today. I don't think his opinion of the Athenians has changed much. I haven't reminded him that my former master, a very honourable man, was a native of the city...

April 12

With few expressions of regret, Paul has told us all that we shall be leaving Athens tomorrow. He's very disappointed at the general rejection of the Good News, although there are several new believers including one member of the Council, Dionysius by name. There's also a woman named Damaris, but I've not found out her background.

April 13

Our next destination is to be the provincial capital, Corinth, about two days' journey to the west. I'm not sure that I'm really looking forward to this, as the place has a reputation throughout the empire for general lawlessness and vice of every kind. I suppose it's what you would expect from a major seaport, with its focus of worship being Aphrodite, goddess of lust. You have to admit that Athens is slightly more civilised than many places. Still, Paul regards Corinth as a key target area for spreading the Good News, on the route to Rome, and apparently, there's a good-sized Jewish element in the population to start with. The road we'll be travelling along is well made and heavily used, and we expect the journey to be fairly easy.

April 17

This city is huge, throbbing with the constant din of trade and commerce, and everyone apparently too busy to stop and talk. While Athens succeeds in demonstrating some of the finer points of Greek culture, Corinth seems to have embraced with gusto all things Roman, especially the philosophy of "live now, never mind the consequences". I'm concerned for Paul, who seems a bit off colour, and admitting to feeling weak in both body and spirit. We've found some fairly cheap but basic accommodation in a fairly quiet district, and Paul is resting for a while. Rufus has been sent off to locate the synagogue, as Paul naturally wants to start his work here with the Jews. We're all very hungry, as we left Athens with little food or money, and don't see any immediate change to our circumstances here.

April 19

Paul said he felt better this morning, and went on his own to the synagogue quite early on. He returned about mid-day, cheerful and much more positive. I asked what had happened.

"Listen to this!" he exclaimed. "You know how I've been so frustrated for weeks at not being able to earn my keep. Well, I've just met a couple of tent-makers: Aquila and Priscilla, his wife. They're devout people who came here from Rome when Caesar issued that decree expelling the Jews after the riots, and they are really excited about the Good News of the kingdom. Also, their business is expanding and they desperately need a skilled pair of hands to help them. Gather up your stuff, because we're all moving in with them. We'll make a weaver out of Rufus yet!"

It's a relief to see Paul restored to his normal positive self.

May 11

Getting the message across is not easy here. Paul is clearly not well, being annoyed with himself for lacking his usual stamina. There's no obvious cause, apart from overwork. His tiredness seems to be affecting his ability to think clearly, and I've never before known him to struggle for words when teaching. In spite of this, he has been at the synagogue every Sabbath since our arrival, reasoning from the Jewish scriptures that Jesus of Nazareth is the fulfilment of all the prophecies about the

Messiah, and giving instruction (as the Lord himself did) on things pertaining to the kingdom of heaven.

May 14

Wonderful news today: Crispus, the leader of the synagogue, has become a believer, with the rest of his household, but there is the now all-too-familiar growing antagonism from the stricter Jews in the local community. On the other hand, through the tent-making business, Paul has met a lot of Aquila's contacts, including non-Jews, and some of them have shown a genuine interest in the Good News of Jesus. The most common reaction is one of amazement when he says that no one is "too wicked" to be accepted by God – and in Corinth, that's certainly saying something!

More than once, I've heard Paul getting quite worked up about this, saying, "Believe me! I know full well what I'm saying is the truth! I was a murderer, going out of my way to persecute anyone who showed allegiance to the man known in life as Jesus of Nazareth. That same Jesus, in truth alive again from the dead, confronted me and showed me his love. Because he died for my sins, I don't have to, and what else can I do now but urge you to believe that the same can be true for you too? It doesn't matter who you are or what you may have done – put your trust in Jesus as Lord and you'll be accepted by God, whether you think you deserve it or not!"

Stephanas, a well-known businessman in the city, has invited us all to his home for a meal tonight. It seems that he still has a lot of questions he needs answering.

May 16

We're all very relieved at Timothy's return from Thessalonica. He turned up this afternoon, saying that he had felt the Lord very close to him on his travels, and it had all been plain sailing. The brothers there would seem to be as fond of us as we are of them, and they're growing in faith and love. This news has given Paul a real boost, and when his mood lightens we all feel better.

May 18

There was another happy reunion this afternoon. After what seems an age, Silas and Titus are back with us, bringing that cloak I left behind. There was no Urbanus, as he'd felt he should stay on with the church at Beroea. In his place is Aristarchus, a member of the church in Thessalonica and of quite noble birth. His family have sadly disowned him on account of his new faith, so he's pledged himself from now on to assist Paul in spreading the Good News. I think he'll be a real asset, as his obvious good breeding and level of education will make him very acceptable to those we might encounter in the higher levels of society.

Titus spent quite some time explaining why it had taken them so long to reach us. It seems they had delayed their departure from Beroea in order to carry on instructing the believers there. A lovely bunch of people, by all accounts, they wanted to better understand why the Good News really does form the climax to everything that the Jewish prophets foretold in the scriptures.

On the down side, we have been disturbed by something Aristarchus has said, about some believers in Thessalonica clearly being very confused about some of Paul's teaching. It seems that a number have even given up working at their jobs, as they think that Jesus Christ is returning any day now to finish setting up his kingdom. I don't think that Paul and Silas ever gave that impression. It's a real pity we had to leave there in such a hurry.

It then took our friends longer than expected to reach Athens, as they made the most of every opportunity to tell people about Jesus of Nazareth and his resurrection. This sometimes meant staying in one place for several days at a time. Then when they did reach Athens, they were slightly amused by gossip concerning the "madman" who'd brought the city almost to a standstill with his announcements about a Jewish preacher who, he claimed, had been raised from the dead because he was the Son of God...! It wasn't hard to get the information that he'd since gone off to Corinth. I think Paul is slightly cheered by the fact that there would seem to be at least a few people in Athens who remember something of what he said.

With all that excitement, I nearly forgot to mention that Stephanas and his household have received Jesus as Lord of their lives, and were baptized in his name yesterday. As so often happens, there was quite a party afterwards.

May 20

Rejection: it's happened again. Paul, as usual, has been making it his priority to present the message of the kingdom to his Jewish "brothers", and they've finally turned against him most emphatically. You'd think it would break the man's heart. He got very angry today, and shouted at them, "Your blood be on your own heads! You've had your chance. If you're going to be so thick-skinned and cloth-eared, I'll take my message to the outsiders, and with a perfectly clear conscience before the Lord!" Then he went to the house next door, where Titius Justus lives, to cool off for a while.

May 21

This morning, Paul told us of a vivid dream he had in the night. The Lord spoke to him saying, "Keep your spirits up! Carry on with the good work of sharing my Good News, even if they try to silence you. Remember, I am with you in this, and I will protect you, for there are many who are mine in this city – even if they don't know it yet!" Paul is now convinced that we have to stay here for the long term, so I'll have to seek opportunities to practise my physician's craft to earn my keep. Although it's a rich city, the poor are always with us, and they are often the sick too.

May 22

Aristarchus is being sent back to Thessalonica on a rather urgent mission. Silas and Paul are very concerned that the church there needs both encouraging and setting on the right track regarding some misconceptions. Obviously, Paul can't go there himself, much as he'd love to, so he's dictating a letter that Timothy is writing down. Aristarchus is to take it to Jason, with instructions for it to be read out to everyone in the church in Thessalonica.

With persecution from the Jews obviously being the main problem they face, Paul's basic message to the Thessalonians is, "Don't be surprised by what you're experiencing. You've seen how they've persecuted me! Stand fast in your faith, serve one another in love, live in such a way as to please the Lord, and look forward to the day when He comes back to restore the kingdom of Israel. But, and it's a big but, remember that no one knows when that will happen – so in the meantime, do your best to live honourably in the world as it is." I hope they'll find that helpful.

June 3

In view of his profitable business association with Aquila and Priscilla, and now having the company of Timothy, Paul is urging me to return to Antioch for a while. He said that as I'm now sixty years of age, I should look after myself a bit more. And it's the best time of year to be making the sea crossing. I said to him, "But you're not a well man. You know that! Who's going to look after you?" He insisted that he will be alright, having learned how to live with his affliction, although there are times when the pain is evidently severe. I'm torn between staying here with my friends and going home to see all the old faces and places again. I suppose the truth is that I'm not really needed here at the moment. Paul and the others are far more effective than I am in sharing the Good News with the Corinthians.

June 5

I will be leaving Corinth tomorrow. We've heard there's a suitable ship in port at Cenchrea, bound for Seleucia by way of Crete and Cyprus. Paul has recently written several letters, one of which I'm carrying with me for the Antioch church. This evening we'll be having a farewell meal with Crispus, Chloe, Achaicus and some of the others. I still have mixed feelings about leaving Paul. Life in Corinth hasn't been as bad as I'd imagined, and Titus seems really at home here.

My journey home and the subsequent lengthy interval of normal life don't warrant a detailed account. Our ship stopped off at Heraklion in Crete for two nights, and I was pleased to note that the Good News had arrived there somehow. It didn't sound as if the group of believers there was very well organised. I thought, "If Paul were here, he'd soon get them sorted out...!" We heard about the spectacular ruins of a great palace not far from the port, but didn't have time to visit. In port only briefly at Paphos in Cyprus, there was no chance to look for Barnabas or John Mark, but we did meet a Christian couple who said that the church there was in good shape. Paul would have been pleased to know that.

Back home in Antioch, I was very sad to learn that my old friend Nicolas had died and gone to be with the Lord, following a short illness. The number of Christians here had increased a lot, believers from many parts of the empire coming to study with the elders, who are held in great respect. I was surprised and delighted when Aristarchus came over from Thessalonica the following year, with a couple of his friends. He said that Paul had had to write a second letter to the church there, as some believers were still under the false impression that the continual persecution they faced was a sign that the Final Judgment had already begun. Aristarchus said that he wanted to join us on any future travels. I thought that would be good, as he is very agreeable company and a great encourager, just as Barnabas was in the past. I was also very pleased, not to say relieved, when Paul himself returned, greatly in need of a rest.

It took me some time to get up to date with Paul's adventures, and I formed the impression that there'd been a kind of stalemate in Corinth for quite a long while. Paul had worked with Aquila and Priscilla in their tent-making business, instructing them in the faith, and slowly building up a church there – though it was clearly a hard grind, as so many people were coming from a background that was saturated in idolatry and vice. Paul had sometimes found his patience with them running out. He'd avoided the Jews, and they'd shunned him, having previously failed to get any joy from the Roman governor when they'd tried to obtain official support for their opposition to the Good News.

Nothing much had changed until Emperor Claudius appointed Lucius Gallio as the new governor of Achaia province, which prompted the Jews to have another go at getting Paul arrested or expelled for his "subversive" teaching. Gallio was having none of it. A native of Hispania and generally of a fairly easy-going disposition, it was well known that he had a particular disliking for Jews, on the grounds that they always seemed to cause trouble wherever they were. So, in the complete absence of evidence that Paul had committed any sort of real crime, Gallio flatly refused to get involved with what he regarded as a petty Jewish religious dispute. He'd remained unimpressed when the Jews threatened to riot, but the event really soured the air, so within a couple of months Paul decided it was time to leave Corinth. Silas, as a much less confrontational sort of character, had agreed to remain as overseer of the group of believers there, with Titus as his right-hand man.

Having failed to reach Ephesus in Asia province earlier on his overland travels, Paul had opted to sail there from Cenchrea, naturally taking Timothy as well as Aquila and his wife. The distance by sea wasn't far, but they were caught in a violent storm that shipwrecked them on one of the small islands. Thank the Lord, everyone on board was saved, but it was more than a week before they could resume their journey. Once at Ephesus, Paul had spent a few days debating with the Jews in the synagogue, promising to return if the Lord allowed him to, but he was far from well and anxious to get back to Antioch. He left Aquila and Priscilla at Ephesus to spread the Good News of the kingdom in that district.

After a pleasingly uneventful sea crossing, the ship had docked at Caesarea from where Paul and Timothy visited the elders in Jerusalem, spending some months there, before finally getting back here to be received with great joy by everyone in the Antioch church. After that, they had stayed on to help in teaching and building up the church in the city, demonstrating the power and authority of Jesus through the working of his Holy Spirit through them. Some of the miracles had been most unusual.

During this period of relative calm, one thing that caused quite a stir in the city had been the "euaggelion" or joyful announcement of a new Emperor: Nero Claudius Caesar Augustus Germanicus, to give him his full title. He was then[24] only seventeen years of age, keen on the arts, and apparently very much under the control of his mother. Some mystery surrounded how old Emperor Claudius had died. Always eccentric, he'd been behaving increasingly as though he were a god in his own right, and a lot of people – especially Jews – were relieved that he'd gone. Emperor Nero quickly rescinded the law banning Jews from Rome, and many who'd fled to the provinces had gone back home, including quite a number who were now Christians. People seemed generally more hopeful under the new regime. However, my impression of Roman emperors so far was that they rarely, if ever, lived up to their promise...

With a significant break from his travels, Paul found himself in much better health. He'd remarked on how much he was appreciating regular eating and sleeping habits, but began talking about getting on

---

[24] 54 AD

the road again before winter set in. The general plan appeared to be to go overland to Ephesus, revisiting the churches in Galatia on the way. Paul would be taking Timothy, Aristarchus and maybe one or two others, but I'd told him that I didn't feel free to join the group at the time. My main concern was Anakletos. Already older than his years, he was afflicted with a wasting disease that didn't seem to respond to any treatment. To my profound regret, I could not save him this time, and he died in his sleep one night in the early spring of the following year. Sharing in the family's grief, I did what I could to help them. Then, after the appropriate period of mourning, I sent a message to Paul, for when he reached Ephesus, that I was now free to join him.

Travel Diaries – Series III

March 22[25]

After hearing nothing from Paul for well over a year, we'd all become very concerned. Then, two days ago, the letter arrived with my sailing instructions. Just time to stock up with some of Paul's favourite tonic. I'm now in Seleucia looking for a ship that will take me to Ephesus, having been brought downriver by some friends from the Antioch church, who have their own small boat. The Harbour Master's advice is first to sail to Cyprus, on a vessel due to leave tomorrow morning. Then from Paphos it should be easy to get one of the regular sailings between there and Ephesus.

March 23

We set sail on time, but progress is slow with only a very gentle breeze. I don't mind if the sea remains fairly smooth the whole way. I shall probably use the some of the journey time to continue collating my notes on the life of Jesus of Nazareth, before I start forgetting what people have told me! I really need to get back to Jerusalem sometime, and talk to more of the people who knew him while they're still alive.

March 30

The journey so far has been uneventful, and still rather slow, with not enough wind to fill the sail for two whole days. The oars have been in use quite a bit. I had no time to visit anyone in Paphos, as this ship I'm on now was in port making ready to set sail for Ephesus, by way of

---

[25] 57 AD

Rhodes and Cos. By chance, two of my new travelling companions are followers of Jesus, members of the church in Paphos, so we have had lots to talk about. John Mark has visited them a few times, being now held in high regard by the island's Christian community, and preparing to start travelling farther afield once more. Sergius Paulus was recalled to Rome to take up a new post there a few years ago. No one's heard anything from him since. I trust that he is well.

April 2

In port, on the island of Rhodes, having made up some time in the past couple of days. Every visitor here has to see the remains of the giant statue of the god Helios that once towered above the harbour entrance. Standing over a hundred feet high before it was destroyed by an earthquake more than two hundred years ago, it was regarded by many as one of the wonders of the world. It had been visible from miles out to sea – an amazing combination of art and engineering. But the pride of the people of Rhodes had such a mighty fall!

The ship's captain says we'll have to wait for a change of wind direction before we can move on again, so we're stretching our legs on dry land for a while. There is much about the place that is beautiful, especially the display of blossom on the trees at the moment, but it's overshadowed by a sense of faded greatness, with many once fine buildings in disrepair. I gather that the place has rather fallen out of favour with Rome, and is now clearly something of a backwater. Because of that, the island is apparently popular with political exiles wanting to keep a low profile. So different from the centre of learning and culture that it once was.

April 4

We're rattling along now with a following wind, and should reach Ephesus within two or three days at this rate. I am really looking forward to catching up with Paul and the others again, as well as seeing the sights in the city I've heard so much about.

April 6

Ephesus, at last! Even while we were still some distance offshore, we could clearly see it had been built on a grand scale. Now, close up, we can appreciate just how truly enormous some of the buildings are – one of the passengers on the ship told me that the world-famous temple of the goddess Artemis is more than a hundred and twenty paces in length, and made of the purist white marble. No doubt I shall be able to see for myself fairly soon. In contrast to Rhodes, the city positively reeks of power and wealth, its large dockside area teeming with merchants from every corner of the empire.

Word of my arrival has been taken by a messenger to the synagogue, where someone should be able to tell us where Paul is at the moment. Some people I've spoken to in the port have heard about him and the news of Jesus and his new kingdom. But their deity is Artemis, and they seem quite happy with that!

Later: I'm to wait here at this tavern until someone comes to fetch me. It seems that Paul regularly uses the lecture-hall of someone named Tyrannus as his base for teaching, having fallen out with the Jews at the synagogue a while back. It still puzzles me why, so often, the more the Jews learn about the Good News of the kingdom, the more their attitude hardens against it.

April 8

I've really enjoyed catching up with everybody, and hearing about their adventures. So much to write down. Timothy has grown a beard! Meanwhile Aristarchus has shaved his off, and looks about ten years younger as a result. I'm delighted to find that Stephanas and Achaicus are here from Corinth, with a lovely woman called Phoebe, who's been involved in running the church in Cenchrea. She has her own business and travels widely, sourcing herbs and spices. She seems to spread sunshine wherever she goes – I must get to know her better.

With everybody chipping in different parts of the story, it hasn't been easy to track exactly what happened when, but I understand that Aquila and Priscilla had to do a fair amount of "corrective" teaching early on, as some people were not getting a fully accurate story about Jesus. This had come about following the arrival in Ephesus of an Alexandrian Jew called Apollos. They said he was an excellent speaker and did a great job convincing many Jews from their own scriptures that Jesus is the Messiah. However, although he taught "baptism for repentance" after the manner of John the Baptizer, he didn't understand about "baptism in the Holy Spirit". Aquila and Priscilla were very tactful about this, taking Apollos to one side and successfully explaining things to him in full. He'd then headed off to Corinth with letters of introduction to the church there.

Sometime after that, reports had come back of factions forming in the Corinthian church, with a "Paul Party" and an "Apollos Party", among others. There was also disturbing news of decidedly immoral conduct on the part of certain church members, so Paul had sent them strongly-worded letters (since he couldn't go there in person). I understand that he'd spelled out in plain language the evidence for the resurrection of the Lord Jesus, and how we should live in the world while awaiting his final glorious return. I'd like to have read those letters. Paul's wisdom has grown so much through his experiences of taking the Good News to those who've not heard it yet. I never tire of listening to him.

Paul himself told me how, soon after he arrived here in Ephesus, he came across a group of about a dozen new Jewish believers (presumably taught by Apollos) who, far from being baptized in the Holy Spirit, had never even heard that there is a Holy Spirit. He quickly put them straight on that score, and as soon as they'd been baptized in the name of the Lord Jesus, they all began speaking in heavenly languages and declaring inspired words from the Lord. Quite a party ensued, by the sound of it.

Paul also explained to me that he'd been anxious to have people he knew and trusted based in Rome, to help lead the growing number of believers there. In the end, he'd persuaded Priscilla and Aquila that, while he would miss their company greatly, he felt that they should go home to Rome, now that the new regime had made that possible.

Aristarchus has been telling me about some really unusual miracles, with Paul not even needing to place hands on sick people for them to be healed. There are many reports of how sufferers too ill to come to him had been made completely whole just by being touched with one of Paul's handkerchiefs...! Life has clearly been quite interesting here recently. I've made notes of other exciting episodes, which I must write up in full, when I get the opportunity.

––––––––––––––––

Editor's Note

For the sake of brevity, the diary entries for several months are not included here. Not that there was nothing worth reporting, but much of it would have been repetitive. The effects on people of the Good News of the kingdom of heaven often followed a similar pattern, both in terms of demonstrations of the power of the Holy Spirit, and also of rejection (even persecution) by those who found it all too much to handle.

November 6[26]

Paul has started talking about being back in Jerusalem next spring, but wants to revisit Philippi and Corinth over the winter. There has been such a change in the spiritual atmosphere here in Ephesus. I think it was triggered by that episode with the Jewish exorcists who tried to deliver a man from possession by an evil spirit "in the name of Jesus whom Paul preaches". Apparently, it was almost comical – the man beat up all seven of them (sons of a Chief Priest, they said), shouting out, "Jesus I know and Paul I know! Who do you think you are?" This event was widely reported in the city, one result being that the name of the Lord Jesus is now held in great awe. Many people have turned from their occult practices and become believers, and recently there was a massive public bonfire of books of magic, and such stuff.

November 8

Timothy and Erastus are being sent on ahead to Philippi, with letters to Lydia, Clement and the other leaders in the church there. The rest of us will probably be leaving Ephesus to join them within a week or two. After more than six months, I feel as though I've been here long enough now. It's been an interesting time, for sure.

November 13

Today saw major trouble in the city, after a long period without serious disruption to our work. It wasn't the Jews though, this time. With so many people becoming followers of Jesus, there's been a drop in demand for the icons and souvenirs related to the city's renowned cult of Artemis. The silversmiths have been losing a lot of business. One of them, Demetrius by name, acting as spokesman and shop steward, addressed a rally in the city centre. He launched into a tirade against us (but mostly against Paul) for not only undermining their trade, but bringing the name of the goddess Artemis into disrepute. He got

---

[26] 57 AD

everyone there very stirred up, and there was a lot of chanting of, "Great is Artemis of the Ephesians!" Then they seized Gaius and Aristarchus, dragging them into the theatre to appear before the City Council. Some of us mingled with the huge crowd that gathered there, hoping to see what might happen, but Paul was kept well out of the way on the advice of some friendly senior officials. The way the mob was behaving, I was afraid he'd be lynched if they got their hands on him.

Fortunately, the immediate danger seems to have passed, thanks to some very sensible but firm reasoning by the grammateus[27] presiding over the hearing. He pointed out that the men they had brought to court had committed no crime, nor blasphemed the name of the divine Artemis, declaring, "She is, as you are all well aware, still the guardian of our great city! If Demetrius and the others have a genuine grievance, the Magistrates' Court is the place to go. As for now, if this pointless commotion doesn't end immediately, we're all in danger of being charged with riot over today's events." Then he sent everyone away – no buts!

Thank the Lord, Aristarchus and Gaius were unharmed, but you could see that they'd had a horrible experience. We hear that the die-hard Jews are taking advantage of the circumstances, again trying to make trouble, and Paul is very upset over the whole business. It looks as though we'll be leaving here sooner rather than later.

November 16

Paul has had a last meeting with the church here, urging everyone to stay firm in their faith in Jesus the Messiah. Aristarchus and I have been overseeing the logistics of getting things packed up for the next stage in our journey, which will be along the coast road to Troas, giving us the chance to visit some new places with the Good News – although it seems to be spreading by word of mouth quite quickly now, as new believers take it with them wherever they go. There'll be six of us this time, as Paul has asked Tychicus, Trophimus and Gaius to join the party.

---

[27] clerk to the Council

November 20

In Troas for a few days. The Lord has opened several doors for Paul to preach and teach, but we were expecting Titus to be here, and there's no sign of him. We're all very concerned, Paul seemingly especially distracted.

November 26

Still no sign of Titus. It's been agreed that we'll sail tomorrow, weather permitting.

November 30

It's lovely to be back in Philippi, after a notably uneventful journey, blessed by a steady following wind. It was the first time at sea for Trophimus, and he was thrilled when our ship was accompanied by a school of dolphins as we sailed out of Troas. We made a brief overnight stop on Samothrace, with a very swift passage from there to Neapolis. As before, we are staying in the city with Lydia, who has apparently been making a great fuss over Timothy and Erastus – treating them like the sons she never had, I suppose. The church is flourishing here, and Paul is evidently very happy to be back, although it's probably not for long this time. He's still worrying about the church in Corinth.

December 3

Paul cheered up visibly today with the arrival of Titus, bringing better news from Corinth. Unhappily, though, it seems there are still some people there who are openly challenging Paul's authority and integrity as a spokesperson for the Lord. As a result, he's in the process of writing another letter, to get certain things off his chest so that there'll be no need for a face-to-face row when he arrives there himself. While spelling out the facts to silence his critics, he also wants to encourage the church there because of the improvements that he's heard about. Titus will take the letter back to them as soon as possible.

December 10

Paul, Timothy and the others are preparing to head off to Corinth, by way of Thessalonica and Beroea. Erastus and I will be staying in Philippi until further notice. We'll be lodging with Clement (whom I like immensely), as Lydia has to make one of her occasional business trips across to Ephesus and will be away for quite a while. The idea of travelling by sea in the middle of winter doesn't seem to bother her at all, but I suppose it's not a very long journey really. I intend to catch up with writing my book, and have been promised some work in one of the local medical practices.

To keep my narrative concise, I'm not including many details of life during the next few months. After Paul had left, things were on the whole pretty quiet, apart from one night in the middle of winter when our sleep was suddenly disrupted by an earthquake. This brought back memories... All over the city, people were rushing out of their homes in their nightclothes, and it seemed as though every dog in the empire had started barking! However, it was all very brief, and fortunately caused little damage apart from some tiles falling from roofs. Later, I learned how Julia Agricola, one of the older ladies in the church, had been very upset that a decorative glass flagon had shattered on the floor after wobbling off its shelf. It was much treasured, having belonged to her mother, who gave it to her when she (Julia) moved to Philippi with her late husband on his retirement from the army.

Although there were no winter epidemics, I was kept quite busy treating a range of ailments, and found that there is a big demand for the herbal remedy that Paul finds so helpful when his digestion is giving him trouble. People were more than happy to pay, so I've been earning my keep, which I know will receive Paul's approval. My account of the life of Jesus of Nazareth is coming on well, but I really need to get back to Jerusalem to collect more first-hand detail before I can finish it off.

April 3[28]

A letter arrived from Paul today, at last, bringing news and greetings from them all in Corinth. The journey through Macedonia and Achaia went well, he says, with several stops to encourage people in the churches on the way. The number of believers keeps on growing, which is great news. Although the Corinthians had received Paul's letter some weeks before he turned up, there were still some serious issues requiring his personal attention, so that's where they've been for the past three months. However, the church there now seems to have friends in high places, as a senior figure in the city's administration – another Erastus – has become a believer. A wealthy man, he's been personally funding projects for the benefit of the community as one way of serving the Lord. Things in Corinth seem more settled now, and the letter says that they are planning to sail from Cenchrea back to Ephesus in the near future.

Judging by the date on the letter, they should be there by now, but we'll wait to hear from them before leaving Philippi. I must say that I've really enjoyed my stay this time, and have got to know Theron very well. For a former jailer, he's surprisingly well-read and has a gift for teaching, holding classes for the sons of a number of freed slaves in the city. No discipline problems, of course!

April 8

We were all taken completely by surprise this afternoon by the appearance of Paul, Timothy and an enlarged group which included the young Beroean, Sopater (who'd warned us of the conspiracy by the Jews on our first visit to Macedonia), as well as Secundus from Thessalonica. Apparently, there was yet another plot against Paul's life, and at the last minute they'd changed their plans for sailing from Cenchrea, coming back overland to Philippi instead.

As always when we get back together again, conversations lasted well into the night, with Paul apparently able to function perfectly well on as little as three hours' sleep. Probably not good for him – but he's a grown man, so why should he heed his doctor's advice…? He told me that he'd written a long and detailed letter to the Christians in Rome, realising that he wouldn't be going there himself on this trip after all. I

---

[28] 58 AD

know that he misses Priscilla and Aquila, who've opened their home in Rome as a meeting place for the church, which apparently includes quite a number of people who are there from other provinces too. Well, as the saying goes, "All roads lead to Rome!"

April 13

Paul and his seven fellow-travellers took to the road for Neapolis this morning. Tomorrow, they hope to sail for Troas where they will wait for us. The rest of us will be leaving Philippi straight after the Passover.

April 21

Everything's arranged for us to leave tomorrow, so we spent today with Theron and his family. They laid on a special supper, and invited quite a number of our brothers and sisters from the local church. We really enjoyed ourselves, celebrating friendships that will last for ever, even if we never meet again in this life. Erastus has revealed a completely new aspect to his personality, causing much mirth with his impersonations of certain persons not present. There was music, and much dancing. Later to bed than is good for me...

April 25

Safely back in Troas, the whole party now reunited. It seems that Paul is itching to leave tomorrow with a few of the others, taking the overland route south to Assos. The plan now is for us all to rendezvous there in a couple of days' time. We've celebrated the Lord's Supper with the church here for the final time (on this trip, at least). Paul feels that there is still a lot of teaching that he needs to give, so it looks as though it's going to be a long session this evening. Feeling very tired, I've chosen to have an early night.

April 26

I was right about the long session. At breakfast, they told me how it had been approaching midnight and Paul was still talking, with potentially fatal results. A young man, Eutychus, sitting listening at a third-floor window, was overcome by sleep and fell headlong to the ground below. They thought he was dead. Paul broke off from his sermon, picked the youth up gently in his arms, and said, "It's alright, he's still alive. He'll be fine!" Then after a short break for refreshments, he carried on with his talk, not finishing until this morning. He'll be back on the road before noon, after no sleep at all last night. I do worry for him.

Apparently, Eutychus is none the worse for his tumble, and quite unaware of what happened. A very fortunate young man! His family are very relieved – hardly surprising, really.

April 27

Tychicus, Erastus and I are about to sail for Assos, where Paul, Timothy, Trophimus, Sopater and Aristarchus will join our ship tomorrow or the day after. Secundus will soon be sailing back to Macedonia, while Gaius is to return to Derbe. We spent some time first thing this morning praying for one another, asking the Lord to keep us all safe on our respective journeys. It's always very hard to say farewell to such good friends. I heard Paul talking about "going home" – I think he meant Jerusalem, rather than Tarsus.

April 28

We made excellent progress sailing along the coast from Troas, with a helpful breeze from the north and beautiful scenery all the way. Assos itself is perched on a hill overlooking an excellent harbour, sheltered by the island of Lesbos, which offers boats at anchor almost total protection from bad weather. Paul and the others were awaiting us as planned. We've crossed over to Mitylene on Lesbos, where we're stopping for the night.

May 1

After a bit of island-hopping, by way of Chios and Samos, but sailing right past Ephesus, we are now in Miletus, where we're to stop for a few days. Paul is anxious to be back in Jerusalem in time for the Feast of Pentecost, and feels that if we go to Ephesus we might have more trouble with the Jews. Instead, he's sent word to the church leaders there to come to him here. After much prayer and soul-searching he has decided that his "adopted son" Timothy should go back to Ephesus and be part of the leadership team there. That's making him particularly sad, but he's certain that it's what the Lord wants. Erastus will go too, at least for a while. Trophimus thought about returning as well, but feels that his place is to be beside Paul for the time being.

May 5

Rather like Rhodes, Miletus has seen better days. The locals maintain that in the past the river was much more suitable for trade than it is today, but shifting sandbanks in its very winding channel now create a hazard for even quite small ships. Some of the buildings in the city are looking a bit tatty, although the great theatre is still well used. We visited it, noting with interest a wall plaque inscribed "Place of the Jews, who are also God-fearing". This made Paul shake his head in sorrow at the thought of how far his kinsfolk have strayed from the straight and narrow.

May 6

An eleven-strong delegation of Christian leaders arrived from Ephesus this afternoon. They reported that the church in Ephesus is growing strongly, and is regularly sending out men and women to teach and encourage the other churches in the western part of Asia province. There is now scarcely a place left in the region that has not been reached with the Good News of the kingdom of Jesus the Messiah. Well, he himself said that the message would be taken "to the ends of the earth"…

May 7

There were many tears and affectionate embraces this morning, as we prepared to embark once more. Last evening, we all gathered to hear Paul speak to the Ephesian church leaders. I could see that he was unusually emotional as he reminded them of how he had given himself in service – body, mind and spirit – to them for so long, and of his tears shed on their behalf. "What I emphasised then and emphasise now," he declared, "is that all of you, Jews and Greeks alike, should repent and place your faith in our Lord Jesus. I know that I am now under compulsion to go to Jerusalem, and the Lord alone knows what will happen to me there. He has told me by his Holy Spirit that I must expect imprisonment and persecution wherever I go, but that doesn't bother me as long as I can complete the task that I've been given of spreading the Good News of the grace of God. I do know that none of you assembled here today will see me again in this life." (Some of those present burst into tears when they heard that.)

Then he warned them to be on their guard against people bringing false teaching or trying to create division between believers, speaking of "savage wolves falling without mercy upon the flock". Finally, he commended them to the Lord as "shepherds" consecrated to God and charged with caring for the weak and the poor. I could tell that his heart was torn between the desire to stay with them and the strong sense of urgency about returning to Jerusalem.

A large crowd from the church came down to the harbour to see us off. Timothy put on a brave face as we left him, understanding the responsibility that has been placed upon his young shoulders, but we didn't even try to be cheerful in the situation. We all know that things are going to be different from now on.

May 8

An overnight stop on the island of Cos after a swift journey with a following wind. No chance to look around – off again early this morning. The wind dropped right away but we've managed to reach Rhodes just before nightfall. I'd been hoping to show the others some of the ancient city's famous sights, but that won't happen now.

May 9

A steady west wind today. Our ship made good speed, and we docked here at Patara (on the south coast of Asia province) when the sun was still quite high. For some distance, we were accompanied by dolphins, which seemed to enjoy showing us how fast they could swim, riding on our bow wave, side-slipping to disappear under the hull, and then coming up on the other side of us. Watching them was a delight, and added enjoyment to an otherwise rather dull journey. We knew when we boarded the ship that it would bring us only this far, as it would then be making the return trip to Ephesus with a fresh cargo. Tomorrow we're going to have to look for another vessel that will take us on to Cyprus or, even better, directly to one of the ports on the coast of Phoenicia.

Paul seems very calm and contemplative at the moment. I'm glad that our travels have been going so smoothly, as delays and disruptions would have affected him badly. I'm very aware of the many threats and challenges he has faced on his journeys during the last few years, so it's good that it's plain sailing for once.

Although none of us has been here in Patara before, the Good News has been brought by others, and we've met several people who are in the small local church. They recommended these overnight lodgings in the upper part of the town, where we've been well received and given an excellent supper with wine they said was from Cyprus. Made me think of Sergius Paulus...

May 10

We've found a ship preparing to sail to Tyre. Well, it was actually Tychicus who found it. Being rather younger than some of us, he is a fast walker, and often gets the job of delivering messages. He was down by the harbour this morning, taking some exercise and keeping his eyes open for a suitable passage. When he got back he said, "I suddenly noticed a small patch of purple on the quayside. It looked like dye that someone had spilt. 'Costly slip, that,' I thought. I looked up, and there was a ship unloading its cargo. On the off-chance, I asked one of the crew if they'd come from Tyre, as I know that's where the dye is made. He said yes, and they'd be heading back there tomorrow. When I asked about taking passengers with them, he said, 'You'll have to ask the boss.'"

Not only have we met "the boss", who is in the dyeing business, but we've also found in him a long-term acquaintance of dear Lydia. When we explained who we are and why we've been travelling, he insisted that we should accept his offer of free passage home. Yet again, the Lord seems to have gone ahead of us on our travels.

May 11

We're expecting to be at sea for three or four days, depending on the wind. The ship is well-laden with a crew of fifteen, the same number of passengers, and a cargo that includes wine and fine linen cloth. Tychicus and Aristarchus have said they're quite willing to each take an oar if the wind fails. What it is to be young and fit...!

The ship's crew are all very friendly – a mixed bunch, including the blackest African I've ever seen, with eyes like a pair of moons in a dark night sky. From Nubia, someone said. One of the others, Simeon Bar-

Judah, grew up in a fishing village near Caesarea. He's very distinctive for having just the thumb and one finger remaining on his left hand, but I haven't had the chance to find out what happened to the others. He's much more keen on telling me how, when he was young, he'd heard a lot of stories about Jesus of Nazareth. He himself became a believer only after he met someone in Caesarea called Philip, who'd encountered Jesus himself after he'd come back from the dead. Simeon's not an educated man, but full of the Good News, and he feels that it is his happy duty to seize every chance to share it with the people he meets on his travels. He says that he often finds his fellow Jews to be very sceptical about it all, while many of the others want to cling on to their familiar pagan gods. Paul is already giving him teaching and encouragement, pointing out that he won't always see for himself the results of his obedience to the Lord. A lesson there for all of us, I think.

May 13

Good progress so far. The coast of Cyprus was clearly visible away to the north when we woke up this morning, but has now dropped below the horizon. There is emptiness around us in all directions. No sea birds, no dolphins, and just a gentle swell on the sea. The next land we sight should be the Phoenician coastline. I've enjoyed the chance to do some more work on my book. I hope in due course to cross-check some of the details of Simeon's stories.

May 16

After the peacefulness of our journey, the sheer volume of noise here in Tyre is almost exhausting. The port is so busy that our ship had to stand off for several hours before we could find a berth. The city still enjoys some independence from Rome, and like Corinth, it's a very cosmopolitan place. There's been a community of Christians here from the early days – quite a number of disciples came here when the persecution began. Simeon knows some of them well, and says he'll introduce us.

May 17

They're a lively crowd here! Everyone's thrilled to meet Paul in person, having heard of how he's been taking the Good News to the far corners of the empire. All four of us are staying in the house of Alexander and Rhoda, who moved here from Jerusalem when the city became too dangerous for anyone labelled as a follower of the Lord Jesus. They've enjoyed more than twenty years of peaceful married life in Tyre, and are well-known in the city for their generous hospitality to all and sundry.

Alexander has an interesting story. He had once been tipped for a senior role in the priesthood in Jerusalem, and had known of Saul of Tarsus, being about the same age. His prospects changed radically when he became a believer in Jesus as the Messiah, after the miraculous healing in the Temple precinct of a forty-year-old man who'd been lame from birth. Simon Peter and John had been instrumental in that, and Alexander was present when the Council subsequently interrogated the two of them over what had taken place. His considered response had been that the Lord God was clearly at work in a new way! Already widowed for four years, he was a friend of John Mark's mother, in due course marrying Rhoda, who was one of her servants. (I love the way class distinctions don't seem to apply in Jesus' kingdom!)

Rhoda's lovely; still blessed with the red hair that gave rise to her name. She's told me the amusing story (no longer embarrassing for her) of how Simon Peter had turned up late one night at the house where she'd worked. This was soon after he'd been arrested and put in prison awaiting execution. James Bar-Zebedee, older brother of John (whom I remember meeting in Jerusalem), had been put to death not long before, so everyone was in a terrible state of fear and distress. Quite a number from the local church had gathered at the house, and were praying far into the night for Peter's safety.

To pick up the story in her owns words, "We were in the back room, and things had quietened down for a minute or two. Suddenly there was this loud banging on the front door, giving everyone such a fright! The first thought was that the Temple police had come to arrest some more of us. One of the men there said, 'You go, Rhoda! You're young and pretty – they won't harm you. See if you can sweet-talk them into going away...' So I went heart in mouth to answer the door. Before I even reached it, I recognised Peter's voice yelling, 'Let me in! Let me in!' I was completely dumbfounded by that, and instead of unbolting the door for him, I rushed back inside shouting, 'It's Peter! It's Peter!' Nobody believed me at first, saying that I was mad and that it was really his ghost – he must have been killed already. But it was him, alive and well! I thought he would tell me off for being so daft at the time, but all he did was gently tease the others about me being the only one to show any courage. Peter had been such a rough diamond in the early days. It was amazing to see how gentle and wise he'd become in a very short time."

Peter's experience of being woken in prison by an angel, who led him out past guards and through doors that opened of their own accord, gave much encouragement to the believers at the time. The official enquiry after the event never came up with an explanation for his mysterious disappearance from the prison, but the elders in the church had decided that it was no longer safe for Peter to stay in Jerusalem. He'd stepped down from his position as leader, and had kept well out of public view for quite some time.

I've heard other stories from people who lived through those early days of excitement and persecution, but this was one of the best. I'm so grateful that the Lord arranged for us to come here to Tyre.

May 23

Paul says we must move on to Jerusalem without delay, to be there before Pentecost. Several times at meetings this week, people felt the Spirit prompting them to warn Paul about the danger of going there, but he is unwavering in his purpose. Nobody needs to be reminded that Jesus' own death came about through his decision to go to Jerusalem, against the advice of some of those closest to him.

We have found a small ship that's going to be calling in at various places down the coast, and it seems that the whole congregation of the church in Tyre – women and children too – have come to see us off. We've made some good friends here, and will miss them.

May 24

The ship has been tied up at Ptolemais[29] for today, which has given us the chance of a quick meeting with the small group of believers here. They want us to stay so that Paul might teach them, but we have to sail on to Caesarea tomorrow morning.

---

[29] Acre

May 25

Safely at Caesarea well before evening: immediately struck by the size of the harbour, which they say has room for three hundred ships. Our seafaring days are over, at least for now, and we're all very thankful to the Lord for his protection on our long journey from Ephesus. We're staying at the home of Philip, whom I have known about for many years. I hadn't made the connection, but he's the same Philip that Simeon told me about on our sea-crossing to Tyre. Along with my friend Nicolas, he'd been one of the seven church administrators appointed in Jerusalem in the early days. While delighted to get news of Simeon, he was very sad to hear that Nicolas had died – but said, "I know we'll meet again at the resurrection. There'll be a lot of catching up to do!" Although widowed, he has four daughters, all still unmarried and living in the home – so we'll be well looked-after.

May 26

I took the opportunity to do a bit of sightseeing this morning. Unscrupulous tyrant that he was, Herod the Great famously had tried to outdo the Romans with the scale of his building project here, including a vast theatre. One problem was there was no local supply of fresh water. To meet that need, Herod had ordered the construction of a ten-mile aqueduct, which has been greatly appreciated by the Roman occupiers in more recent years, as this is now where the Governor has his official residence. I can understand why he might not want to be in Jerusalem more than he has to, constantly rubbing shoulders with the Jewish Council. That said, a fair number of the senior Roman officials here are quite sympathetic towards Christians, and some have themselves become believers. They've told me the story of how Simon Peter came here more than twenty years ago and shared the Good News of the kingdom with a God-fearing centurion and his household. When I asked, "Was that Cornelius?" they said, "Yes – did you know him?" I said, "No, but I heard the same very interesting tale from Peter's own lips some years ago!"

May 27

I had a long and engrossing conversation with Philip this morning. He's told me about some of his amazing adventures after he'd been given specific instructions by the Holy Spirit. This was during the turbulent times after his fellow deacon Stephen had been so unjustly put to death. Philip had known all about Saul of Tarsus, and the campaign to stamp out what some people called the cult of the Nazarene. He is very proud of his daughters. "The Girls", as he calls them, are blessed with far more than just domestic skills. They're all enabled by the Holy Spirit not just to hear what the Lord says, but to speak it out as well. Not surprisingly, they are held in high regard in the community.

It wasn't through them, however, that the Lord sent word to us this time. Today, the Lord's Day, we had a surprise visit from Agabus – the same Agabus who had come to us in Antioch and prophesied the great famine that happened more than ten years ago. Not a hair on his head now though. This time, quite dramatically, he took the belt from around Paul's waist and lashed his own hands and feet together with it. Then he declared, "These are the words of the Holy Spirit! The owner of this belt will be bound up like this by the Jews in Jerusalem and handed over to foreigners!"

We've all been very distressed by this, and are urging Paul not to go on. He, on the other hand, seems more resolute than ever, saying, "All this weeping and wailing isn't in the slightest bit helpful to me! For the sake of the name of the Lord Jesus, I am quite prepared not only to be bound, but to die in Jerusalem – if that's what must be." I know that when he's in this frame of mind, there's no point in pursuing the matter, so we've just said, "Whatever the Lord wills," and left it at that.

May 28

It's with mixed feelings that we're packing our bags and collecting provisions for the last leg of our journey. At twenty miles a day, we should be in Jerusalem before the end of this week. Two donkeys have been provided to help with transport, and three of the younger men from the church are coming with us to make sure we arrive safely! (As if we're not used to travelling...)

June 2

A frustrating delay today, a sudden violent thunderstorm forcing us to take shelter for several hours, but we still expect to reach Jerusalem tomorrow.

June 3

A great burden seems to have lifted from Paul's shoulders. Jerusalem was always his second home, and he seems enormously relieved to be back in time for Pentecost as planned. Our young guides have served us well, bringing us safely to the house where we're to stay while in the city. Our new host is Mnason, who is a Cypriot by birth but has lived here in the city for many years. Like his friend and compatriot Barnabas, he became a Follower of the Way in the very early days. Word of our approach must have preceded us, as he'd arranged a gathering of men and women from the local church, who gave us a very warm welcome. Tomorrow, we are once more to have a meeting with James, our Lord's brother, now greatly respected as leader of the church here.

June 4

Today's meeting went on longer than expected, and involved all the elders of the church. James is known to all as "the Just", because of his wisdom and integrity in dealing with matters relating to the laws and traditions of the Jews, insofar as they affect followers of Jesus. He listened intently as Paul gave an updated account of how the Lord has done amazing things among non-Jewish communities in the various towns and cities we've visited in the last few years. Everyone was delighted by what he said, giving heartfelt praise and thanks to the Lord.

James then gave some of the wise counsel for which he's known. In Jerusalem, he explained, there are now thousands of Jews who have become believers in Jesus as Lord, but who still uphold the Law most zealously. "Brother Paul," he said, "they believe that you have been telling Jews living in foreign places that they don't need to bother any more about things like circumcision and the Law of Moses. Some of them still see you as an enemy who is corrupting the purity of their faith. Before they get their daggers out, I suggest this way by which you can demonstrate that you too are an upholder of the Law. We have four men here who've taken a Nazirite vow. Why not make that number up to five, join them in the purification ceremony, and pay for them to have their heads shaved? That should put people's minds at ease. As for our non-Jewish brothers, they already know the conduct expected of them, having received the letter we sent out before."

114

This was accepted by everyone as very sound advice, and Paul was happy to agree to it.

June 5

Paul and the others went through purification this morning, after which Paul went to the Temple to give notice that the duration of his vow will be seven days. He seems very relaxed and happy to be in familiar surroundings again. He told me recently that he's been really looking forward to spending time once more studying the scriptures back where he began in his youth, and joining in the celebrations like in the old days. He doesn't readily boast of his Jewish pedigree, but I know that it matters to him.

June 9

Suddenly, seemingly out of nowhere, we have a crisis. After a few days of relative inactivity with no trouble from the local Jews, everything seems to be now unravelling. This is what I've learned from an eye witness. In the Temple this morning, some Jews visiting for the festival (from Ephesus, it seems) spotted Paul and recognised him. They immediately stirred up a commotion, seizing him and shouting out to everyone, "True men of Israel, come and help us! Here's the man who's been going everywhere spreading the false teaching about our nation, our Law and our Temple! He's even defiled this holy place by bringing a foreigner in here!" (They'd apparently seen Trophimus with Paul in the city and jumped to the conclusion that he'd gone with him into the Temple.) Anyway, a major riot erupted, and a mob dragged Paul out of the Temple and set about beating him to death on the spot.

Just occasionally, one is thankful for a Roman army of occupation. With the barracks right next to the Temple precinct, a contingent of troops led by a senior officer was on the scene very quickly. The assailants retreated from a very bruised and bloodied Paul, who was assumed to be some kind of troublemaker or criminal, so he was arrested and bound with chains. When the officer in charge tried to ask who this man was and what he'd been doing, so many people in the crowd started shouting so many different things that he couldn't establish the facts, and simply gave orders for Paul to be taken back to the barracks. The mob surged forward again, yelling, "Kill him!" Some of the soldiers picked him up and carried him away for his own safety.

As they were going up the steps to the barracks, Paul spoke to the officer. "Sir," he cried, "may I have a few words with you?"

The Roman officer, surprised to be suddenly addressed in formal Greek, replied, "What? You speak Greek? I thought you were that rabble-rouser from Egypt who's been such a nuisance recently!"

"Oh no, sir," continued Paul. "I'm a Jew and a citizen of Tarsus – by no means an insignificant place in the empire. Will you let me speak to the people?"

Obviously interested, the officer gave his consent.

The reports from people at the scene make it clear that Paul delivered the same amazing testimony that I've heard so many times over the years – how the risen Lord Jesus changed the course of his life. From being a fanatically zealous protector of the purity of the Jewish faith, he'd become the one commissioned by the Lord to spread the Good News that his kingdom was now open to foreigners too. When he got to that point in the story, there was (as so often happens) a violent eruption of protests from his audience of Jews, with further shouts of, "Kill him! That man doesn't deserve to live!" The commander promptly ordered his men to take Paul inside, and the doors of the barracks were slammed shut.

What happened next I can relate in Paul's own words, as a few of us were able to visit him this afternoon, although he's still in custody in the barracks. (He's probably safer there than outside...) All things considered, he's surprisingly cheerful, and I was relieved to learn that he has been given some medical attention and a proper meal with wine.

This is his account of what ensued behind closed doors. "Orders had been given that the truth should be extracted from me by a good flogging. A centurion was supervising while two soldiers strapped me up in preparation for the treatment. Then I said to him, 'What's the law regarding flogging a Roman citizen such as myself, and in particular, one who has not yet faced trial?'

"At that, the centurion went to his commander in a state of panic, and the senior officer himself immediately came in and asked, 'Is it true that you are a Roman citizen?'

"'Indeed it is,' I replied.

"'It cost me a small fortune to buy my citizenship,' he said.

"'Well, sir,' I said, 'my citizenship is by birth.'

"At this, he instructed the soldiers to untie me at once, ordered them to say nothing to anyone about the episode, and took me into his own apartment where the garrison medical officer dealt with these cuts and bruises. I think Claudius Lysias – that's the commander's name – is essentially a good man, and he's determined to find out what it is that the Jews are accusing me of doing. He's ordered the entire Council to assemble in the morning, and will be there in person to oversee my formal hearing. Don't worry on my account. I know that the Lord is standing by me."

After such an eventful day, and with great uncertainty over what will happen tomorrow, many of us have spent a long evening in prayer. I don't really feel like sleeping.

June 10

The hearing today ended abruptly and in chaos. Paul was allowed to nominate three friends to attend, so I have a personal record of what took place. Things didn't start off very well, as Paul opened his defence by saying, "Men and brethren, all my life to the present day I have lived with my conscience clear before the Lord God..." at which one of the Council members ordered that he be struck across the mouth. Paul was livid, and shouted, "May the Lord God strike you, you whitewashed wall! You purport to be trying me according to the Law, yet you order me to be struck in contravention of that same Law!"

It was promptly pointed out that the Council member who gave the order was in fact Ananias the High Priest. But Paul couldn't have known that, since he'd been appointed to his post some years after Paul had left Jerusalem and wasn't wearing any official insignia. Paul simply didn't recognise him. After apologising unreservedly for committing such a serious breach of protocol, Paul was allowed to carry on. Recognising that in the Council there were representatives of the two opposing religious sects, Sadducees and Pharisees, he declared, "I am a Pharisee, and my family have been Pharisees for generations. It is because I hold on to a sure hope of the resurrection of the dead that I'm on trial now!"

Predictably, that instantly divided the Council. Sadducees deny that there is any such thing as an afterlife, let alone resurrection, while it's a key element of what Pharisees believe. Immediately, some of the latter jumped up in Paul's defence, which led to violent arguments breaking out across the floor of the hall. The Roman commander summoned a squad to rescue Paul, and we went out with him as he was hurriedly escorted back to the barracks. Nothing has been resolved.

June 12

This morning things have taken a turn for the worse, if that's possible.
We've learned of a conspiracy involving some forty Jews who are opposed to Paul's teaching. They've taken an oath not to eat or drink until they've killed him, which is grim news indeed. The plan seems to be for the High Priest to demand that Claudius Lysias brings Paul back to the Council for a further hearing, with would-be assassins in waiting to pounce on him before he gets there. This vital inside information comes from Paul's nephew, Jonathan – thank the Lord that he was where he was at the time! Being a relative, he was allowed to visit his uncle very early this morning, getting to him while it was still dark. After he'd told Paul of the plot, Jonathan was taken to the commander's quarters, where he repeated the story. Naturally keen to forestall anything that may spark a riot, Claudius Lysias thanked him for the information and said, "Not a word to anyone that you've been here!"

But Jonathan's come back and told us, saying that his uncle is in remarkably high spirits. He says that Paul told him that the Lord came and stood by him in the night, saying, "Be encouraged! Just as you have spoken up boldly on my behalf in Jerusalem, so also you must speak up for me in Rome." That doesn't look very likely, the way things are at the moment!

We've all been advised to stay out of sight until further notice. Several of the church elders are with us, and we have been praying to the Lord that he will cause good to come out of what seems a very bad situation.

June 17

This may be my last entry for a while. Just after we'd had our midday meal, there was a loud banging on the door, always a cause for alarm. In fact, there were two Roman infantrymen there, simply bearing a message from Paul. The commander has given orders for a large contingent, including cavalry, to escort him as prisoner back to Caesarea. We (that is Aristarchus, Tychicus, Trophimus and I) are to go too, and must be ready and packed by dusk, when a squad of soldiers will fetch us. For reasons of security, we shall be leaving the city during the evening and travelling overnight. We will be provided with horses, which is reassuring.

June 18

We've made rapid progress and arrived here in Antipatris soon after dawn. I'm surprised how quickly I've got used to being on horseback again, though I have to admit to being a little saddle-sore! (I have my medicine chest with me at all times...) The centurion in charge says that we should be safe now, so after some rest and refreshment most of our armed escort will be heading back to Jerusalem. The cavalry troop will stay with us until we reach Caesarea, under the command of another centurion, who is carrying a letter for Governor Antonius Felix. Its contents are no secret, and I've been able to make a copy for my own records.

A fair statement of the situation, it explains how Paul is a Roman citizen whom he'd rescued when the Jews were trying to kill him. (But no mention of the official flogging that was about to be administered...) As the accusations against Paul all relate to their own Jewish religious laws, there is no valid reason to keep him in custody. However, because of private information about a plot against his life, he's being sent to Felix for protection, and if the Jews want to pursue their case, they must present it to him as Governor.

We'll be in Caesarea before nightfall tomorrow. The cavalry maintain a very brisk pace!

June 19

I never expected to see inside Herod's Palace, which now serves as the Governor's official residence. It's an unashamed display of wealth and power, and one can't help wondering how much it cost the people of Judea in taxes and hard labour. Paul has been given some very reasonable quarters here, and can receive any visitors he likes. He is under house arrest with guards on duty at all times, but we're told that this is chiefly for his own protection. I know that he has no intention of trying to escape. As soon as we arrived he was presented to the Governor, who has read the letter (apparently with little show of interest) and says that he will hear the case as soon as Paul's accusers arrive.

June 20

With Aristarchus, I spent much of today with Philip and several of the other leaders of the church in Caesarea. They've had reports from others that since word got around that Paul was back in the area, there has been a marked increase in the agitation levels among the Jews against followers of Jesus. There seems to be a general strategy to try to divide the church, setting Jewish believers against all the rest, and reviving arguments over the sanctity of the Law of Moses. I suppose we shouldn't be surprised, as the same thing has nearly always happened when we've taken the Good News to places we've visited in other provinces.

Some of us will be visiting Paul every day. With enforced idleness, he's taking the chance to dictate some letters. This is partly to spell out to people in the different provincial churches what is the really Good News about Jesus of Nazareth. Far from denying or belittling the Jewish scriptures, he explains that in Jesus' death and resurrection from among the dead, the Lord God is showing that everything that was written before by the prophets is true, the promises made to the Jewish nation are being fulfilled, and in this new age that has begun, everyone – Jew and non-Jew – is invited to join in the party. (That last part is what seems to cause all the upset.)

June 26

The court hearing took place today, at last. Ananias the High Priest, this time in all his ceremonial regalia, arrived last evening with a group of senior Jewish leaders and a barrister specially selected for the role of prosecutor. This man, calling himself Tertullus (though not, I believe, a Roman), clearly has a high regard for his own skills as a performer. He stood up in court as if taking the stage, smelling strongly of oil and soap, and speaking that way too! He's evidently being well paid to sway the Governor's position in favour of his employer.

He took every opportunity to address Felix as "Your Excellency". I think that this had little effect. As one of Emperor Claudius' freed slaves, infamously unscrupulous in advancing his own career, the Governor is known to be willing to take a bribe. He administers Roman justice cruelly and often indiscriminately. Apparently, he has spies everywhere, and is kept well up-to-date about what is going on in his province.

Listening to the way Tertullus carried on, you might have thought that Felix was the Emperor himself, personally responsible for the peace and prosperity enjoyed by the people of Judea! (Though I don't think Tertullus has asked the people of Judea what they think about that...) His prosecution case was the same as the one presented to the Jewish Council in Jerusalem, now with frequent loud endorsements from members of the Council. The prisoner in the dock, Tertullus declared, was deliberately disturbing the peace among Jews throughout the world, as ringleader of a heretical sect that would even desecrate the Holy Temple. "I beseech you, Your Excellency. Ask him yourself!" he added.

At the invitation of the Governor, Paul then spoke in his own defence. Having had plenty of time to prepare, his address was comparatively short and to the point. Far from stirring up unrest among the people, he explained, a couple of weeks ago he had gone back to Jerusalem after an absence of several years to take part in the festival. Also, he was bearing charitable gifts from others for his own people. There was no trouble at all until the visiting Ephesian Jews started the hue and cry – and here he was quite emphatic: "In my opinion, it is they who should be appearing before you here with their accusations, if indeed they have any valid charge against me. As it is, I don't see a single one of them present in this court!"

The only possibly controversial statement Paul made was that while he upheld the authority of holy scriptures as the unalterable Word of the Lord God of Israel, he admitted to worshipping him according to what some call the Way, which others call heresy. "My hope in the Lord is the same as theirs – the resurrection of all people, good and bad – and to that end, I strive to live my life with a clear conscience before God and man."

Felix didn't seem very impressed by the prosecution and has adjourned the case indefinitely. Judging by what he said in his summing up, he is surprisingly knowledgeable about the Way and evidently feels that this is just another instance of the Jews trying to stir up civil unrest. He's instructed the centurion responsible for Paul to keep him under house arrest with the same conditions that he has had so far. That's the good news. The bad news is, of course, that the charges have not been completely dismissed.

June 27

Tychicus, Trophimus and I spent some time today with Philip and other leaders in the Caesarea church. Nobody knows what we should do now. It's very frustrating, especially for Paul, I imagine, as he loathes being shut up, unable to get out and spread the Good News.

June 28

Nothing happened. People are complaining about the weather, which has become unusually hot, even for midsummer. I have done some more writing. It was a good reason for staying inside where it's a bit cooler.

June 30

A couple of us spent the afternoon with Paul, who is still confident that he is where the Lord wants him to be for the present. Yesterday he was summoned to the Governor's quarters, but it wasn't to be given any news or judgement. Felix, with his wife Drusilla (a high-born Jewess), wanted to question him in detail on why he is so convinced that Jesus is the Messiah. Paul needed no second bidding, and told us how he was able to spell out not just the historical context for his new faith, but also how it has to result in a complete transformation of one's attitude to all aspects of life, both personal and in the wider community. Everything was going smoothly until he began explaining how every person will one day be placed before the judgement seat of the risen Lord, at which the Governor became quite agitated, dismissing Paul with the words, "That's enough for now! When it's convenient, I'll send for you again."

Knowing what motivates Felix, Paul has told us that the chief reason for him being detained is the hope that someone will pay a substantial ransom in exchange for his freedom. Not much chance of that – none of us has much money at the moment.

July 1

We got a message from Paul this morning, asking us to visit. He told us that one of Philip's daughters had been woken by a prophetic dream from the Lord, saying that he (Paul) must learn to be content in his present situation, as it will last for many months. Paul has readily accepted this as a message from Jesus, as it confirms the way he has been feeling himself. He thinks that I should take the opportunity to go back home to Antioch for a while. He is in quite good health, is being well looked after, and intends to get some letters written while he has plenty of time on his hands. He wants Trophimus to stay around, while Tychicus, who has developed a real love of travel, will be his messenger. Aristarchus, he says, will be going back to Thessalonica with another letter for the church there, when he's finished it.

As always when I'm about to leave Paul, I have very mixed feelings.

Editor's Note

In order to keep this account concise and relevant, it was decided to omit the diary entries for a considerable period that followed. The story resumes almost two years later, with new developments concerning Paul and his travels.

May 14 [30]

At last, I've had a letter from Paul asking me to return to Caesarea as soon as possible. Tychicus arrived with it today, the news being that Antonius Felix has been replaced by Porcius Festus as Governor of Judea. There's hope that this might lead to Paul's release, with Rome beckoning once more. Tychicus also brought a gift of money to pay my fares. This was quite unnecessary, as I've been well paid for my services as physician to several prominent families in the city. Once we've packed my bags, naturally to include my medicine chest and the book I'm writing, we'll be going down to Seleucia to find a ship that's heading south along the coast. I'm now very anxious to be reunited with Paul – Tychicus says he's been unwell recently – and we should be there by the end of this week.

May 19

There was a joyful reunion this afternoon. Trophimus and Aristarchus have been back here for some months, and are both well. Paul looks more than two years older, having lost most of his hair, but with a

---

[30] 60 AD

longer beard to compensate. His face is also looking much more lined, but he has the same old fire in his eyes. Straight away, he wanted to hear all about what I've been doing, while I was equally keen to listen to him. The situation, as I understand it, is now this: Tension between the Jewish authorities and Rome is at an all-time high. Obviously keen to start off on the right footing, Governor Festus went to Jerusalem just three days after he'd taken up office two weeks ago. He's expected back at any time. Paul is hoping that he'll be able to speak to him as soon as possible. He is visibly excited at the prospect of freedom and the chance to fulfil his dream of taking the Good News to Rome.

MAY 20

Festus arrived back here shortly after noon. Paul didn't have to wait long to see him – two guards came and took him to the Governor's quarters within the hour. All four of us visited him this evening, and heard from his own lips some news that has filled us with dismay.

In Jerusalem, far from having forgotten about Paul, the Chief Priests and Jewish Council had immediately raised his case with Festus. They demanded that as a special gesture of friendship to them, he (Paul) should be taken back to Jerusalem to face his accusers. In the event, the only concession made by the new Governor was that Paul would remain under house arrest, in Caesarea. If the Jews wanted to present their case, he said, it was up to them to observe protocol and send a delegation to the Governor's residence, once he was back there.

When we were asking Paul what he thought he would do now, he said, "Since the Lord has told me that I shall take the message about his new kingdom to Rome, I believe that he will make that happen – and I trust his wisdom as to how it happens! I know that everything works out for the best for those who love the Lord, who have a calling within his plans for the world." We have been slightly reassured by his confidence in this situation, although it's hard to foresee a happy outcome.

MAY 21

The delegation from the High Priest must have been hard on the Governor's heels yesterday, as Festus summoned Paul for his court appearance very early this morning. We were admitted, being recognised as his companions by the officer in charge. Apparently, he's from the Tarsus area and Paul speaks well of him, being fairly certain that he knows of his family.

The trial, if it can be called that, was just as riotous as the previous hearings had been, the Jewish delegation shouting all manner of accusations, but with no facts to substantiate them. Paul didn't attempt to argue with them, but simply stated, "In no respect have I committed any offence, either against the Jewish Law, or against the Holy Temple, or against Caesar."

Festus, clearly not wanting to get on the wrong side of the Jewish authorities right at the start of his term of office as Governor, spoke directly to Paul. "Are you willing to go to Jerusalem and have your case heard in my presence there?"

Paul's response was unequivocal. "This is Caesar's court, and this is where I should be judged! You are perfectly well aware that I have no case to answer with these Jews. The fact is that if I had committed some crime, even deserving the death penalty, then I would not try to evade sentence. However, since there isn't a shred of evidence to support the accusations that these men have made against me – and I'm not prepared to be used by you as a way of placating them now – I appeal to Caesar himself!"

I was very concerned that with such straight-talking Paul might have alienated the Governor, who immediately retired to a side room with some legal advisers. After what seemed like an age, he emerged, resumed his seat and made the pronouncement, "Since you have appealed to Caesar, then to Caesar you must go!" There was an eruption of protests from the Jerusalem delegation, but Festus gave orders for the courtroom to be cleared and for Paul to be taken by a squad of guards back to his quarters and kept under constant watch.

It now looks as though we shall be heading for Rome after all. Not quite in the circumstances that we'd hoped for, and with no indication of when we shall actually leave here.

May 26

The crowds were out today, with a state visit to Festus by King Herod Agrippa, accompanied by Berenice, presented as his Queen although everyone knows that she's his sister. Agrippa, in his token position as local ruler, seems to be doing a very good balancing act, generally getting on quite well with both the Romans and the Jewish leaders, although there's a lot of tongue-wagging about his personal relationships. I hadn't previously realised that Drusilla, wife of former governor Felix, is another of Agrippa's sisters. Looks to me like another of those "convenient" marriages that happen within the ruling classes.

May 27

When we went to see Paul as usual this morning, he told us that he's now got to appear before Agrippa, who has heard about him and wants to meet him in person. Festus has outlined the situation to the King, explaining that Paul will remain here in custody until such a time as he can be sent to Caesar. Preparations are being made for him to be presented at a lavish state occasion tomorrow. Paul has insisted that his friends should be allowed to attend, as witnesses, so I should be able to give a first-hand account of everything.

May 28

Everybody who is anybody in the city seems to have been invited to the hearing before the King. One of the larger halls in the palace had been decorated with banners and wreaths, and Agrippa and Berenice dressed in their royal finery were escorted in by a guard of honour, as well as several city dignitaries. There was a lot of bowing, and speeches of welcome and mutual admiration (mostly very insincere, I feel), before Festus gave orders for Paul to be brought in. Standing before the court, flanked by guards, he wore his heavy chains with calm dignity.

The Governor has evidently landed himself in a tight spot, without any obvious way of getting out of it. Politically, it's vital for him to avoid antagonising the Jewish leaders, while at the same time not contravening strict rules regarding the treatment of a Roman citizen. I listened with interest to his explanation to the King, Queen and assembled officials of how Paul had come to be in his custody – in a way pointing the finger of blame at his predecessor. He, Festus, could find no offence in Paul, let alone a crime deserving the death penalty, as demanded by the hard-line Jewish faction.

"I have summoned the man here today," he continued, "in the presence of you all, and especially you, King Agrippa, so that you may subject him to questioning and perhaps help to draw up some charge against him. It seems ridiculous to be sending him to Caesar for no reason at all!"

Agrippa then said to Paul, "We grant you leave now to speak on your own behalf."

Paul has had plenty of time to prepare for an occasion such as this. He spoke clearly and without hesitation for a long time. He gave details of his own strict traditional Jewish upbringing in the city of Tarsus, and then of his time as a disciple of Gamaliel at the School of Pharisees in Jerusalem. He described how that led to him becoming a zealous persecutor of anyone known to be a follower of the man known as Jesus of Nazareth. Members of that sect claimed that he had been raised to life from among the dead, as the Promised One foretold by the prophets and longed for by the people. That was something that he most emphatically did not believe. Then on the way to Damascus, armed with arrest warrants, he was literally stopped in his tracks by a personal encounter with the risen Jesus, an event which changed him and the course of his life. Since then, all he has done is urge people everywhere to allow the Lord to change them too, from the inside out, explaining that the Law of Moses and the writings of the prophets all really point towards the suffering, death and resurrection of the Messiah, who is this Jesus of Nazareth. "He is the first to rise from the dead, and that means we've entered a new age where there is real hope for all people, Jews and non-Jews alike!"

At this Festus shouted out, "You've taken leave of your senses, Paul! All your learning has driven you mad!"

"Permit me to disagree, Your Excellency," Paul responded, not raising his voice at all. "Far from being mad, I am speaking the simple truth about things of which the King is very well informed. Tell me, King Agrippa – do you believe what the prophets have written? Well, I know you do…"

At this Agrippa interrupted him, crying out, "Much more of this and you'll be turning me into a Christian too!"

Paul replied, "Whether it takes much more or only a little, my earnest desire before the Lord is that you, and all who are hearing my words today, might be in my position – only without these chains!"

The court was then adjourned. Agrippa, Berenice and some of their retinue disappeared into a side chamber with Festus, Paul was led away by the two guards, and we were left wondering what would happen next.

Late this evening we finally got word of the verdict. Paul was found not guilty of anything deserving imprisonment, let alone the death penalty. Festus thinks he's mentality unbalanced (!) but no threat to society. King Agrippa would have had him set free, but for the fact that he has appealed to Caesar and therefore has the legal right to a hearing in Rome. Let us hope it's not long before we set off. We've all got a feeling of being imprisoned here now.

Editor's Note

The diary entries for the next fifteen weeks record little of special interest, with Paul being detained in the same comfortable quarters at Herod's Palace, and free to receive any visitors who called. Various friends arrived and departed bearing letters. At times Paul became impatient with the authorities, but had to accept the official stance that they had to wait for the right ship heading in the right direction. Unusually stormy weather in August had further delayed things. Luke notes that he has all but completed his first book about the life and works of Jesus of Nazareth, and hopes that it might in time be copied for circulation to churches in the provinces.

Travel Diaries – Series IV

September 12[31]

We have at last got reasons to be cheerful. After the two previous false alarms that we were about to take to the seas once more, this time our departure is guaranteed. A centurion from Caesar's own regiment, Julius Niger, originally from Cyrene in North Africa, has been assigned the task of ensuring that Paul and several other prisoners are safely delivered to Rome. Out of uniform, Julius is a kind and reasonable man, and he paid a special visit to Paul this morning, asking him how many of his party would want to sail with him. I think that it will be Aristarchus, Tychicus, Trophimus and me. Paul was adamant, when we were discussing things a while back, that I should accompany him on this most important journey. I think I'm still fit enough…

September 15

I had for some reason thought we'd be boarding a naval vessel for a direct passage to Rome. In fact, we find ourselves on board a cargo ship that came here from Adramyttium, on the coast of Asia not far from Troas, and which is heading back there with several ports of call on the way. We now accept that we might be facing quite a long journey. Julius has asked us to keep our luggage to a minimum, as the ship will be heavily laden from the start. Also, we will have to transfer to another vessel at some point on the journey, and so don't want to be carrying too much stuff. I've got a small medicine chest, and my recent journals very carefully wrapped to keep them dry. With a big sail and a south wind, we are now making good progress.

---

[31] 60 AD

September 16

We've spent the day in Sidon, having arrived here at first light. Quite a bit of cargo had to be shifted, and the captain wanted us all out of the way while that was going on. Julius was happy for us to go ashore without escort, instructing the eight soldiers under him to take the opportunity for a little land-based rest and recreation. Paul has enjoyed some hours in the company of friends, and we've all been given a good meal. Ship's rations sometimes leave a lot to be desired... We shall be setting off again in the morning.

September 17

With quite a stiff breeze from the south-west, at the moment we're heading more or less straight for Tarsus. However, it's not one of our ports of call, and Paul doesn't seem concerned at the prospect of bypassing his home town. His mind is focused on Rome, and he keeps talking about people he hopes to see again when he gets there. In spite of sending that very long letter a few years back, explaining to them in detail what following Jesus really means, he's still anxious for them. Even though he is confident that they're being led by people he knows and trusts, like Aquila and Priscilla, the fact that he's not been there himself to be personally involved with them remains a frustration.

September 18

The island of Cyprus appeared on the western horizon this morning, and as we've got closer, we've benefited from some shelter from the wind, which started blowing harder from a westerly point after a short burst of heavy rain last night. Our progress has been slow, and the ship's captain says that our best hope is to set a course that will take us along the north coast of the island. I have been thinking about Barnabas and Mark, and wondering how they are. We have heard that Mark has been doing quite a bit of travelling in his own right, visiting several of the churches in cities in Asia province to provide teaching and encouragement. Apparently, he's written a short book on the life of Jesus, which I would love to read.

September 22

Having left Cyprus behind, we're now heading into the teeth of the west wind. The sail has not been used for three days, and extra pairs of oars have been out, with every able-bodied person (including the guards) taking a turn. I offered, but the captain said I'm too old, and he didn't want to be held responsible for a death on board ship! As always, Tychicus has been showing off his athletic prowess, but got told off for trying to raise the stroke rate and losing his rhythm. The crew are a very good-humoured bunch, and none of us has been spared being the butt of one of their jokes. Sea travel can be monotonous.

September 26

At last, we are ashore again, in Myra, some distance east of Patara where we stopped briefly on our way back from Ephesus. It's hard to believe that was nearly three years ago. I'd heard about this city, famed as the capital of the ancient kingdom of Lycia, and in a way it's surprising that we'd not come here on our earlier travels. Julius Niger has given us shore leave again, since this is where we part company with our ship. To our delight, we've found that not only is there a church here, but they know all about Paul as well, and have copies of letters he sent to some of the other churches in the region. (I hope they're accurate!) We are all staying for the night at what Julius calls the "mansio", although, strictly speaking, it isn't one, not being on a Roman road. It nevertheless compares very favourably with some of the lodgings we've encountered over the years.

September 27

A large two-masted ship arrived from Alexandria today, bound for Italy. Julius says that the captain has agreed to take us, but we shall have to wait for a couple more days, while they unload some cargo and take on supplies. We've all got used to waiting.

September 28

The delay means that we've had quite a good look around the city of Myra, which seems to be prospering under Roman rule. There's a very large theatre, an elaborate pagan temple, and a large number of amazing tombs that have been cut into a cliff face. Down by the harbour are two large statues, which I couldn't help noticing as we arrived. On closer examination, they proved to be images of the famous general Germanicus and his wife Agrippina (both close relations of the Emperor Augustus) who visited the city about forty years ago to great acclaim.

September 29

We received instructions to embark this afternoon. This took some time, as there were more passengers than I expected – well over a hundred of us in all. The ship is already fully-loaded with cargo, including a lot of Egyptian grain destined for Rome, so I cannot imagine that we'll be making much speed. Conditions on board are rather cramped, and I sincerely hope the journey will be soon completed.

September 30

We left Myra at first light. Even though there is a head wind, the ship's captain has decided we must sail while we can as the season is getting late. We fear it may take a month or more to reach Rome, by way of Miletus and Corinth, where we will take on provisions for the second half of the voyage. (I'd love the chance to see some of my friends in Corinth again. I wonder how Silas is getting on...) With the vessel beating slowly against the wind, our zigzag course means that although we've been at sea for nine hours already, the taller harbour buildings at Myra are still visible astern.

October 1

A group of about eight or nine dolphins came and had a look at us this afternoon. They didn't stay with us for long, as we're still making such slow progress against the north-west wind. Tychicus is getting fed up with not being able to take any proper exercise. Although he measured the length of the deck as over forty paces, he finds that other passengers keep blocking his path when he tries to lengthen his stride. Paul has been talking a lot with the ship's captain, who seems to be a man of unusually obstinate temperament. Julius has been playing dice with his soldiers. I've had an interesting chat with a well-educated gentleman who turns out to be a retired medical officer formerly stationed with a garrison on Cyprus, and now returning home to Rome. Many of the other passengers seem to be groups of friends or business colleagues, and mostly keep themselves to themselves.

October 2

The day has been much the same as yesterday, without the dolphins. There's a general air of boredom now.

October 3

Our progress is just as slow, with even more of a head-wind. This morning we could make out the shape of the island of Rhodes to the south. Nobody got very excited. There was a scuffle between two young men this afternoon, with one of them accusing the other of trying to steal from his bag. One of Julius' soldiers separated them very promptly, and ordered them to calm things down. It was in fact all a mistake, as the two men's bags were very similar to look at. I can quite understand why people are getting a bit short-tempered.

October 4

We've dropped anchor for the night off the port of Cnidus on the coast of Asia, a rocky peninsula giving us a little shelter from the north-west wind. I would have enjoyed the opportunity to go ashore and visit the place, with its famous School of Medicine, but it's not one of our ports of call and the captain says we have to press on as quickly as possible.

October 5

Rather than keep on beating slowly upwind, the helmsman and captain have agreed that we should scratch Miletus from the itinerary and head south-west for Crete. Although it's quite a detour from our planned route, we'll have more of a following wind, and should then be fairly sheltered as we head west again along the south coast of the island.

October 6

We're making much better progress now. These modern triangular sails are so good at catching the wind, even when it's blowing from the side.

Everybody seems to have cheered up, now that we're really on the move again.

October 8

This morning we rounded the eastern tip of Crete, known as Cape Salmone. We're all looking forward to getting off this ship to stretch our legs a bit and have some variety in our diet. Most of the dates we brought with us and all the other fruits have been eaten. With grain as the chief cargo, we have no shortage of fresh bread, but there's not much else to go with it. Part of the cargo consists of wine, so we shan't die of thirst!

October 9

We've been travelling quite close to the coast, which is mostly very craggy and inhospitable. A small rocky cove is now offering us a sheltered anchorage, and we'll be spending the night here. There is no sign of any habitation nearby, so the crew haven't bothered to launch the tender and go ashore.

October 10

Our hopes of making faster progress have been dashed, as the wind has backed to a westerly. For a while today it seemed as though we were actually going backwards. The sails were furled, and all the oars put out, every fit person taking his turn, including Paul. I was again excused on account of my age, although I said I was willing to pull my weight, so to speak.

October 13

Today we rounded a headland and were quickly blown into a wide bay, where the helmsman allowed the ship to be carried inshore. We are now at anchor, and most of us have been brought ashore by tender. This place is called Fair Havens, and is not far from the city of Lasea. We shall have to stay here for a couple of days, while the ship takes on supplies. Apart from the ship's crew, we've all been longing to feel solid earth under our feet again. The settlement here is not very large, but they get quite a number of travellers passing through, and there are several places offering good food and accommodation. There's been some discussion that, as we've lost so much time and there's a greater risk of bad weather from now on, perhaps we should sit out the winter here and restart our journey in the spring. I know that Paul would relish the opportunity to meet people from the Jewish community here on the island to tell them the Good News. However, the idea of a lengthy stopover here hasn't gone down very well with quite a number of the passengers, who are banking on getting to Rome before winter.

October 14

It has been decided that as soon as there is a favourable wind, we shall head west along the coast to the port of Phoenix. It offers much more shelter, and is reckoned to be a better place to winter than here, where we're exposed to the westerly gales. Paul was completely against this plan. He said, "Men, listen to me, please. I just know that it's the wrong course of action and you're courting disaster. To set off on this voyage is asking for damage, or even the loss of ship and cargo, perhaps of lives too!" In spite of wishing to get Paul into the hands of the authorities in Rome as soon as possible, Julius has been swayed by what the helmsman and his captain have said. They are, after all, the professional seafarers. I'm trying not to worry, knowing how Paul has always encouraged us rather to be thankful to the Lord whatever our circumstances: "Tell him about the things that are worrying you! He'll give you his peace, and that'll see you through." It's sometimes easier said than done…

October 17

Yesterday there was no wind at all, but today a moderate breeze from the south-east has set in. We're steering a course fairly close to the coast (so at least there is something to look at), and should easily get to Phoenix in a couple of days. There's a more optimistic feel on board now, although Paul is very silent and glum.

October 18

Just a quick entry; writing is almost impossible now. Today a violent north-east wind swept down on us from the coast, so nothing for it but to let the ship run out to sea. This afternoon we got a bit of shelter from the little island they call Cauda[32]. The crew managed to furl the sail and get the ship's tender on board, as well as putting out the sea anchors in the hope that they would slow down our drifting. Some passengers insisted that we should try to make for land, and got angry when the captain said that there was no point. He explained that the island offers nowhere for a ship to take refuge, as the coastline is straight and very steeply sloping. Now, with dusk approaching, our vessel is being tossed on the ocean like a child's toy boat, heading for who knows where. I'm wrapping up this diary with everything else in a leather pouch, and praying that the water doesn't get in.

November 3

After a nightmare journey that no one would ever wish to repeat, and during which we often feared for our lives, we are at last on dry land – we've been told it's the island of Malta. Since I haven't been able to make any diary entries for more than a fortnight, I'll give an account now of what we've been through.

On the second day of the storm, the crew began to jettison some of the less valuable cargo. With no slackening of the winds, the day after that we lost the main mast. Some of the ship's heavier items of gear were thrown over the side to lighten the ship, along with most of the jars of wine. We saw neither sun nor stars, and had no idea in which direction we were being driven. The crew were concerned that we would end up on sandbanks off the African coast. Most passengers were very seasick, and many were in a constant state of terror, praying to their own gods that they might be saved. We prayed to our Lord Jesus, remembering how he promised to his friends that he would never leave them nor forsake them. Paul would not be downcast, and did his best to encourage us all.

After a week the winds eased a bit, but with the ship now badly damaged and still drifting out of control, our hopes of survival were fading. No one had eaten for days. Then one morning, Paul took up a position on the upper deck and began shouting loudly to everyone within earshot. "Listen, all of you! If you'd heeded my advice and not set sail from Crete, you would have avoided this disaster that has befallen you! But now I urge you not to give up hope, as I know that although this ship will be lost, every single life will be saved. How do I

---

[32] Gavdos

know? Last night, standing beside me was a messenger from the God to whom I belong and whom I worship, saying, 'Do not be afraid, Paul. The Lord has determined that you yourself will appear before Caesar, and he guarantees the safe deliverance of every soul with you on board this ship.' So, hold on to your courage – I have total confidence in my God that things will turn out as he has said, even though we may find ourselves shipwrecked on some island."

Two weeks into our ordeal, in the middle of the night, the sailors thought they could hear the sound of breaking waves, an indication that we might be nearing land. They took soundings, and found the water to be a hundred and twenty feet deep. After a short while, they repeated the soundings and found it had shallowed to only ninety feet. Concerned at the prospect of being driven by the wind on to a rocky shore, they ran out four anchors from the stern. Then some of the crew tried to abandon ship, under the guise of lowering the tender in order to lay out bow anchors as well. Paul saw what was happening, and said to Julius Niger, "Stop them! Unless those men stay on the ship, none of us will survive this!" To ensure that no one could leave, three soldiers cut the ropes securing the tender and let it drop away. This act was greeted with cries of horror and anger from those who saw what happened.

We were just starting to make out the first signs of approaching dawn, when Paul spoke up again. "For the past two weeks," he said, "you have been living on the edge. You've not eaten, you're starving and weak. Now you must eat for your own well-being! And remember, not one hair on your heads will be lost!" Then, in full view of everybody, he took bread, gave thanks to the Lord and ate. This encouraged the rest, and after everyone had eaten all they needed, it was decided that there was no point in retaining the cargo of grain, so that was dumped overboard to lighten the ship.

At first light, we could clearly see land – although we didn't know which land it might be – and there was a bay with a sandy beach that looked a promising place to go ashore. It was decided to try to beach the ship, so the crew cut the anchor ropes and those securing the steering oars, and then hoisted a sail on the foremast so that the wind could drive us on to the beach. At first, this seemed to be working. Then suddenly the vessel lurched to a halt, waves crashing over the stern and threatening to smash it to pieces under our feet. The bow had stuck fast in a sandbank.

With land now being only a hundred paces or so away, the soldiers thought they should kill all the prisoners in case they tried to make for the shore and escape. That did, for a moment, really frighten me, and I wondered if Paul would be reaching Rome alive. Thank the Lord – Julius Niger demonstrated why he is a senior officer in the Emperor's elite regiment. Quick-thinking, decisive and bold, he ordered his men at once to sheath their swords and instead to oversee the evacuation of the ship. Any who could swim ashore should go overboard first – Tychicus showing that he could swim just as well as he could run – followed by the rest of us using whatever planks or other debris that might help us stay afloat.

In this way, everybody made it to safety, just as the Lord had promised to Paul. My diary and writing stuff were safe. I'd wrapped the leather bag inside my cloak, and tied that around my neck, managing to more or less keep it floating as I came ashore. Even my wooden medicine chest, which I'd last seen bobbing away in the waves, was returned to me intact by a crew member who found it some way along the shore.

I have no wish to experience anything like that again. To have recorded it with all the details would have made an epic tale to rival any of those written by the Greeks of old.

By the time our cold, bedraggled crowd of survivors had assembled on the shore, we had been joined by a number of the local residents. Our shipwreck had been observed. They were rough people but very friendly. They told us that we were on the island of Malta, and were amazed that we'd survived after drifting all the way from Crete, spending two weeks at the mercy of wind and waves. Seeing our terrible plight, soaked by the sea and now by driving rain, they did everything they could to help us, displaying an unusual degree of kindness. Some went off to get food, and tents to shelter us, while others got a large fire going – there was plenty of wood around. Many of us joined in the task of gathering fuel, and Paul was about to place a large bundle of sticks on the fire when, driven out by the heat, a snake sank its fangs into his hand.

He shook it off, with no sign of any harm, to the amazement of the islanders. They were expecting him to swell up or keel over dead, and after they'd waited for quite a long while and still nothing had happened, they decided that he must be a god! This gave Paul just the opening he needed for explaining who he was and why he was on this journey, and he soon had a small crowd gathered around him near the fire. Out came the familiar yet still amazing story, as he told them the Good News about Jesus of Nazareth who had begun to establish God's kingdom here on earth. As usual, there were some who scoffed and turned away when they heard about his coming back alive after being publicly executed, but others wanted to hear more.

Meanwhile, Julius Niger asked the local people if there was a Roman governor or representative of the Emperor on this part of the island. He found out that we were actually on the estate of the island's chief magistrate, Publius by name, who was himself directly answerable to the Governor of Sicily. With a local man as his guide and two of his soldiers, Julius disappeared into the rain, leaving the prisoners under military guard, although after their ordeal none of them seemed to have the slightest inclination to run away.

It was about noon, and the rain was at last easing off, when Julius reappeared. He brought a warm invitation from Publius for our party to accept the offer of his hospitality, while accommodation would be arranged in neighbouring settlements for everyone from the ship. The prospect of sleeping on a real bed again was most enticing.

That really brings things up to date.

November 6

We are all feeling much better now, after three days of excellent hospitality. Publius is the kindest of men, and has bent over backwards to make us feel comfortable, with first-class catering and generous supplies of wine. As there is no prospect of us leaving for some time, and he cannot accommodate us all indefinitely, he has made arrangements for us to be spread around a number of homes in the area, in groups of two or three. I shall be with Paul and Trophimus, staying with a lady who is, I believe, a cousin of Publius. She's a wealthy widow, and has said that we can stay as long as necessary, which is a blessing indeed.

November 10

It's now certain we shall have to sit out the winter on this island. After a short discussion, it's been agreed that the best plan is for us to make ourselves as useful as possible to the local people in exchange for their hospitality. Word has already got around that I'm a doctor, and I've had several patients to treat, mostly for minor ailments. Paul has offered his services to the manager of a leather-working business, being offered a temporary contract – subject to his work being up to standard! There's no shortage of employment on the land, and Julius has assigned his squaddies the task of rebuilding part of the road network that was badly damaged by flooding a while ago. Not surprisingly, Publius is very pleased about this, having failed to get any response from the higher authorities on the matter.

November 18

After a few very uneventful days, there's been another great storm, with hours of heavy rain and a gale from the south-east. Fortunately, this lasted only a day and a night, although the wind is still strong, from the north-east. Two ships have taken refuge in the sheltered bay where we came ashore. They will both now be spending the winter here. One of them, the two-masted grain ship "Castor and Pollux", is from Alexandria, bound for Italy. We'd been wondering how we were going to continue our journey to Rome. This may be the answer.

November 21

We were woken very early this morning by a loud banging on the door. It was a breathless messenger with the distressing news that an elderly gentleman – the father of Publius, no less – had been taken gravely ill during the night. Could we get to him as soon as possible? Even though it was a three-mile journey in the half-light of dawn, we were standing with a distraught Publius by the old man's side within the hour. I could tell that he was indeed in a very bad way, barely conscious, with a high fever and dysentery.

I was still asking myself what treatment might be best when Paul spoke out loud. "Lord Jesus, thank you that in your death and resurrection you have healed us from all our infirmities. In your name, I command the sickness to leave this dear man's body – now!" Then he laid his hands upon him.

The healing was instant and evident. The patient sat up, stretched and yawned, got off his bed and said, "What's going on here, then?"

Publius doesn't know how to thank us enough. "Anything you need," he says, "just ask!"

A three-month delay in our journey on the island of Malta was not uneventful. But looking through my diaries, I think that including the details is unnecessary in the context of this whole story. Word spread quickly about the miraculous healing, and people came from all parts to be healed from their own illnesses and disabilities. In their gratitude, they showered us with gifts of all sorts. About the time of the midwinter festival of Saturnalia, when there is traditionally a lot of partying going on, we decided to hold a "Jesus festival", giving food and other gifts to the poor people in the community. This was a very popular initiative, and some of us were only too glad to share with others what we felt to be the Lord's blessing on us. In any case, we knew that once we set off on our travels again, we wouldn't be able to take all the stuff we'd been given.

February 25[33]

Several fine, sunny days have provided the first real sense of the approach of spring. There are scores of people here now increasingly anxious to resume their interrupted journeys, Paul amongst them. Hardly a day passes without him saying something about, "When we get to Rome..." In the past week, two ships have called on their way from Libya to Sicily. They reported very good sailing conditions, so there is now a lot of activity in the harbour, ships being stocked up and all the fittings checked to get ready for departure. Paul's professional skills have been called upon more than once in the repair of sails. Julius the centurion (I just think of him as a friend now) has secured a passage for all his prisoners and their companions on the "Castor and Pollux", as we had hoped. It looks as though we should be leaving within the next few days. We have made many friends on the island, and our excitement at the prospect of finally reaching Rome will be tinged with sadness at saying goodbye.

February 28

At sea again, at last. There was a large crowd on the quay as we cast off soon after daybreak, loaded down once more with gifts from well-

---

[33] 61 AD

wishers. Once a few miles offshore, we picked up a good breeze from the south-west, and it didn't seem long before Malta was just a faint smudge far astern on the horizon. The captain has set a course for Rhegium in Italy, and says that we should be there within two days, at the present rate.

March 1

More delays. Last evening, with Sicily visible on our port side, the wind changed to a stiff south-easter, making it impossible for us to hold our course. The captain and helmsman agreed that we should head for Syracuse, on the east coast of Sicily, and the sails were furled to prevent the ship from being blown inshore. The crew manning the oars did a very good job, and it was not yet fully dark when we rounded a headland to see the lights of the city beckoning us in to harbour.

We are now trapped here, the wind blowing fiercely from the east. The word is that we shall leave as soon as possible, but should be prepared for at least a couple of days ashore. Our lodgings are adequate, if not especially clean. (Better than staying on board ship...) Paul isn't treated like a prisoner any more. Julius Niger knows how determined he is to get to Rome, and trusts him absolutely – unlike some of the other prisoners, who have to remain under guard the whole time. Asking around, we've learned that there is a small group of followers of Jesus here. We're told that the Good News first arrived on a merchant ship from Corinth several years ago.

March 2

Paul and a couple of the others had a profitable meeting this morning with several members of the small church here. He reported back that they seem to have been well taught. Their leader, another Alexander, had himself visited Corinth, spending time there with Silas, who was apparently in very good health but handing over more of the leadership responsibilities to a team of younger men.

I went sightseeing with Aristarchus, and came to the conclusion that, rather like Rhodes, Syracuse has seen better days. I have to say that the Temple of Apollo was really impressive, if not especially beautiful. I measured it as sixty paces long, with seventeen massive stone pillars down each side. It's a source of local pride, and one elderly resident we met was very keen to tell us all about it. Built five hundred years ago, it is the oldest temple on the island of Sicily, and the first to be constructed entirely of stone. I then understood why its proportions weren't as pleasing to the eye as some of the great temples I've seen on our travels – the men who built it were still experimenting with techniques at which their successors would become expert.

This afternoon we all relaxed, enjoying the spring sunshine in a sheltered corner overlooking the harbour. The wind seems to be easing, but no ships are yet trying to set sail. Paul talked at length to me about my plans. He's torn between wanting to have me with him, and being concerned that, in view of my age, I should be cutting back on all the travelling. It would be easy enough to find a ship that would take me back to Corinth, he says. I admitted that the difficulties we've faced on this latest journey have made it all a very challenging experience, but insisted that now we are getting so near our destination I shall certainly not be leaving him. "Let's see what happens in Rome," I said.

March 3

We awoke to another glorious morning, with the wind much lighter, though still blowing inshore. Since our ship can to some extent tack against the wind, the captain sent word around that we should all embark as soon as possible to resume our course for Rhegium. Having taken on board a consignment of cheese, for which Syracuse has long been famous, we cast off just before noon. We made rather slow progress, remaining within sight of the coast. The skyline was dominated by the volcano they call Mount Etna, with its constant plume of billowing smoke. I'd heard about this mountain in stories when I was young, but didn't really believe it existed, let alone think I'd one day see it for myself.

We've now laid out the anchors and furled the sails for the night, being only about halfway to Rhegium. We should get there tomorrow with no trouble. Away to the west is an orange glow in the sky, marking the summit of Etna. It's easy to understand why the ancients imagined that one of their gods was under the mountain, working away at his forge.

March 4

It was flat calm first thing today, so the crew were commanded to man their oars. There was a slight disturbance soon after we'd got under way when one oar snapped loudly without warning, the oarsman falling back off his seat with his legs in the air. This caused an eruption of mocking laughter from the crew members near him, but the man took it all in good humour, and was soon provided with a replacement oar. He hadn't hurt himself, I'm happy to say.

By mid-morning a light wind picked up from the south-east, and we are now making good progress under full sail again. The coast of Italy is clearly visible ahead of us, and the captain reckons that we should be safely at anchor in Rhegium well before dusk.

March 5

After an uneventful night on board, we set sail as soon as it was daylight, taking advantage of the wind that was now blowing briskly from the south. Nobody seems to mind that we haven't been ashore, now that we're on the last leg of our sea journey to Rome. "The quicker, the better," seems to be everyone's thought.

March 6

Italy, here we are! Our ship covered the two hundred miles from Rhegium to Puteoli in less than two days, and we're already ashore. It's a beautiful evening, the air fragrant with the scent of flowering trees that I don't recognise. Julius Niger has arranged for Paul and the rest of our party to stay with him in the mansio, while the other prisoners and their escorting soldiers have gone to the barracks.

March 7

Chatting to local people last night, we were delighted to find out that there has been a thriving group of Christians here for nearly ten years. Paul spoke to Julius this morning and we've been given leave to go and meet them, providing we return before dusk. (Julius is clearly still very aware of his assignment to get Paul safely to Rome, and doesn't want any last-minute complications!)

After a little asking around in the marketplace, we were told, "Oh, you're looking for Gaius and Aurelia! Their house is only a five-minute walk from here."

It wasn't hard to find, and when we knocked on the door it was opened by a young woman with golden hair and startlingly blue eyes – Aurelia herself. She almost shrieked with delight when Paul announced who he was, and said, "Oh, we've been waiting and waiting for this day! You know, it seems years since Phoebe arrived from Corinth with that wonderful letter you sent. We expected to see you in person very soon after that, and when there was no further news and no one turned up, we began to fear the worst. We've prayed so much to the Lord that you would come. Oh, we must get the word out to all the brothers and sisters here and send someone to Rome with the news as quickly as possible. Please say that you can stay with us for a few days!"

Paul replied, "If we can, we will. I must inform you, I'm not a free man."

March 8

The good news is that we'll be here for a week, as the military authorities have decided that Julius Niger and his squad should be given a period of leave, after their recent ordeal at sea. Fresh troops will be assigned the task of escorting the prisoners on the road to Rome. Paul is quite sad that he'll have to say goodbye to Julius, who has become such a good friend. After all the conversations they've had, not to mention the miracles that seem to have followed Paul around, we can't understand why this particular centurion has not taken to heart the Good News of Jesus. I suppose he realises that he can't serve two kings, and the Emperor Nero is the one that he sees as holding the power over his own life. You can't win them all!

We've been told that there will be a special gathering of the church on this coming Lord's Day, and Paul has been granted a "late pass", which is good. He is looking forward to holding an extended teaching session – and we all know what that means.

March 13

A new escort for the prisoners has been arranged, and orders are for them to be made ready for departure at first light tomorrow. We've already encountered the officer in charge, a seemingly ill-tempered fellow called Lucius something. He has no time at all for Jews or Christians, and jeered at Paul, saying, "You try telling Caesar that someone else is really King!" Paul didn't even deign to make a response.

March 14

There was a fair-sized crowd to see us off this morning, including many of our new-found Christian brothers and sisters, as well as a motley bunch of onlookers who had collected in order to poke fun at the prisoners. They didn't stay with us for long, as we were covering the ground at a fairly brisk military pace, which I must admit I found very hard to maintain. Definitely beginning to feel my age…

I'm worried about Paul, as he seems unusually low in spirit, considering he's getting so near his long-awaited destination. The soldiers have pitched camp for the night just off the road, and we'll be sleeping under the stars, but the weather is very warm.

March 17

After a fairly uneventful routine of marching by day and resting by night, we reached the Appian Forum last evening. They say just two more days and we should be in Rome! I seem to have got used to walking again, but have serious doubts about my ability to carry on travelling with Paul on any future journeys. He appears to have received a new lease of life and energy, buoyed by the fact that a welcoming party from Rome was waiting for us here. I was absolutely thrilled to meet Rufus and Urbanus again, and there was no end of back-slapping and hugging as Paul was reunited with quite a number of people that he clearly knows well but are unknown to me.

Perhaps the greatest surprise was to be greeted like a long-lost brother by none other than John Mark. We've had no contact with him since he went to Cyprus with Barnabas, after that infamous (and much-regretted) row with Paul. More than ten years on, I didn't at first recognise him through his heavy black beard, but he turned out to be the same boyish Mark underneath. He was very keen to talk, excitedly telling me how he'd completed his book about the life of Jesus. It is already being circulated in Rome and the surrounding area. Would I like a copy? Does he really need to ask! He put names to some of the faces I didn't recognise, and pointed out one couple who are actually members of the imperial household. (I wonder if that will be helpful to Paul…) Grumpy Lucius has undergone a dramatic transformation in demeanour on realising that one of his prisoners seems to be a famous person, with friends in high places. He was last seen trying to curry favour with Paul, and ordered his chains to be removed for the rest of the journey.

With our new escort of excited Romans praising the Lord Jesus for our safe arrival, today's journey had the feel of something like a festival parade. The other prisoners looked quite bemused. Extra provisions had been brought from Rome and we ate very well this evening, with Paul taking the lead as we shared the bread and wine in the Lord's Supper. With a roof over our heads for the final night of our epic journey, we all have a heightened sense of eager anticipation of our own "triumphal entry" into the great city itself.

March 18

Rome at last! It was already growing dark when we got here, but the Appian Way was still busy with traffic – people bringing animals and produce from the countryside for tomorrow's market, several squads of foot soldiers, two centurions on splendid white horses, carts laden with merchandise of all kinds – and so much noise as we entered the city itself.

And there are so many monuments to dead people lining the road, all with inscriptions which challenge my poor knowledge of the Latin language. I'm told that they say things like "Pillar of the community", "Finest wife there ever was", "Great and victorious in battle" and so on, sometimes with prayers to various gods for favour in the afterlife. This made me wonder what kind of afterlife they hoped for – certainly nothing like what we are promised by the Lord Jesus: renewed, immortal bodies in a new and perfect creation in which Jesus will live and rule with us for ever. Sometimes I get a real sense of longing to see that day.

Our party has been split between several different families for purposes of accommodation. The officer in charge of the local barracks has made a very reasonable apartment available for Paul, with a solitary soldier assigned to guard him. Although he's under house-arrest and at present in chains, there will be no restrictions on who can visit him. When I said goodnight to him earlier, I could tell that he is in a very positive frame of mind now. For some unknown reason, the authorities have decided to place Aristarchus in custody as well, but the rest of us are free to come and go as we please.

March 19

My first sight of Rome by daylight has left me almost lost for words. The size of the city, for a start, is difficult to grasp. People are literally living on top of one another, with individual housing blocks five or six storeys high containing as many as forty dwellings and perhaps two hundred residents in all – quite a fair-sized village, really. The Emperor Nero has made his own mark, adding to the already impressive list of great buildings created by his predecessors.

With such a vast city, there is the twofold problem of supplying fresh water and disposing of waste. Thanks to Roman state-of-the-art engineering and construction techniques, solutions have been found for both. Water is brought from as far as forty-five miles away by means of aqueducts, and there is a network of huge tunnels beneath the city that allows the waste to be flushed away. Even so there is squalor amid the splendour, and poverty rubbing shoulders with extravagance. Such a need for the Good News!

March 21

Paul this morning hosted a meeting with senior figures from the Jewish community in the city. He explained how he has come to be here, having been handed over to the Romans by his brothers in the Jewish faith in Jerusalem. "You've probably heard all about it already," he said, "how they accused me of undermining the Law and desecrating the Holy Temple, demanding the death penalty for me. In turn, I accused them of nothing apart from their failure to see that the Hope of Israel, of your fathers and mine, is being realised among us now. And it's that Hope that has brought me here in chains."

It appears that they had not in fact had any reports from Jerusalem about Paul himself, but did know that wherever the new "sect of the Nazarene" (as they called it) arose, it seemed to cause trouble. "Since you seem to be so closely involved," said their spokesman, "we'd very much like to hear what you have to say on the subject. We shall make arrangements for another meeting."

March 23

Paul's house was packed with people today, word having spread quickly in the Jewish community that a controversial preacher from Jerusalem was in town. Paul spoke for several hours at a stretch, with only a short break about mid-day when I was pleased to see him take some refreshment. Continually referring to the scriptures, he explained in detail about the kingdom of God and how it is becoming a reality through Jesus the Messiah. To back up his argument, he often referred to his own experiences of the power of the risen Jesus working through the Holy Spirit. It's a narrative that has become very familiar to me over the years, illustrated with amazing happenings, many of which I've seen with my own eyes.

The reaction from his audience was also familiar: some were won over by his words, while others (the majority, I'd say) scoffed loudly. It's the same story every time Paul tries to bring the Good News to his fellow Jews: many react angrily because what they hear does not correspond with what they've been taught for generations past. They often resent the suggestion that their own understanding is flawed, and as so often happens, today's meeting finally broke down in a series of heated arguments between various Jewish factions. As they began to leave, Paul's parting shot was a quotation from the prophet Isaiah about how deaf and blind God's people are, not recognising Him and so preventing Him from blessing them the way He wants to. "Understand this," he called, "God's promises are for non-Jews as well, and they at least will receive the Good News gladly!" But his passion has never wavered for bringing that Good News to the ears of everyone, whatever their culture, race or creed.

EPILOGUE

Thus my travels with Paul finally came to an end. It soon became clear that he was likely to remain in Rome under house arrest for a considerable time, but there was little chance of him getting bored. There were no restrictions on who might visit him, and people were turning up nearly every day wanting to hear his teaching about the Lord Jesus and the kingdom of heaven. It was often standing room only. Paul being Paul, he insisted on paying a fair rent for his accommodation, earning money by using his lifetime skills and experience at working in leather and textiles. This meant sometimes limiting the visiting hours, as he liked to work by daylight, whereas he had no difficulty at all carrying on teaching long after dark. He was often very tired, but when I once expressed my concern for him, he just said, "Stop worrying, my friend! The Lord gives me all the strength I need. In fact, his power in me seems to increase as I become more aware of my own weakness."

I spent a few weeks lodging with the family of Aristobulus, a well-known doctor in the district, who was very happy for me to help out with his busy practice. After that I was given a room by dear Rufus's mother, who, I gathered, had provided a similar service for Paul during his time in Ephesus some years ago. She's the kind of woman who just has to mother you, regardless of how young or old you may be! She wouldn't accept any rent, so I just used my income as a doctor to make sure that her cupboards were always well stocked. She didn't object to that, and it meant that there was always something on the table that I knew would suit my palate.

Paul often spoke fondly about his friends in the other cities we'd visited over the years, and from time to time received letters and presents from various churches. He was especially pleased by a generous gift, as well as the latest news from Philippi, in a letter

151

brought by one Epaphroditus. This man then became gravely ill, and was at death's door for several days, before recovering to the relief of us all. It was a test of our faith, but the Lord had mercy on him and after a few weeks he was quite fit enough to go home, bearing a letter of encouragement for the church from Paul.

It was Tychicus who was the usual message-bearer, as always enjoying being on the move, whether by land or sea. Paul sent several letters with him, including one to Ephesus for distribution to the churches in Asia, and one specifically for the Christians in Colossae, a town about a hundred miles inland from Ephesus. Paul had never been there himself, but learned about it from a well-educated Greek called Epaphras who had been involved in establishing the church there, and had recently been freed after a period of imprisonment following his arrival in Rome. It seemed that some false doctrines had been spread in the Colossian church, so Paul took great care to spell out the truth, at the same time commending them for the evident Christian love they demonstrated towards one another. Another letter he sent was to the church in the neighbouring town of Laodicea, with instructions that the Colossians and Laodiceans should, after reading them, exchange their respective letters to make the most of his teaching.

Travelling with Tychicus on this trip was a young man called Onesimus, who had a really interesting story. He'd been a slave in Colossae, but had run away after stealing from his master, Philemon, a wealthy businessman and leader in the church there. Having managed to get to Miletus on the coast of Asia, Onesimus then worked his passage on a ship to Rome, where in due course he found himself homeless and destitute, before being taken in by a family of Christians. They started to explain the Good News of Jesus to him, and then had the opportunity to bring him to meet Paul, who immediately took to the young man, "adopting" him much as he'd done with Timothy before.

Onesimus became a firm believer in Jesus as Lord, and made it his vocation to serve Paul in every way he could, in return being treated as a beloved son rather than a slave. However, in time Paul realised that the honourable course of action was for Onesimus to go back to his former master. Knowing that this could result in severe punishment or death for Onesimus, Paul wrote a personal letter to Philemon explaining the circumstances and asking him to welcome back his former slave as a fellow Christian. He even offered personally to pay a fee for the young man's freedom, and to make good any loss that

Philemon had incurred, if that was necessary. We never got a reply, but trusted the Lord that all had worked out for the best.

I had been anxious over the possibility of strained relations between Paul and John Mark, but needn't have worried. They had both changed enough over time to be able to put past differences behind them, and became close friends. Mark had come to Rome after the death of his uncle in Cyprus, having himself become a widely-travelled and well-respected teacher of the Good News.

After we'd been in Rome for two years, a date was finally set for Paul to appear before Caesar. By this time, there were several fairly prominent members of Roman society who had become followers of Jesus Christ and were prepared to speak in Paul's defence. As things turned out, they weren't called upon. Nero, in all his imperial splendour, took one look at the charge sheet, one look at the defendant (appearing very small between two hefty guards), and cried out, "Why waste my time with him! He's neither rebel nor lawbreaker. What do the Jews matter to me, anyway? In the name of Jove Almighty, let the man go, and bring me someone who's actually committed a crime!"

This was better news than we could have possibly hoped for, and very much an answer to prayer. Paul was initially dismayed that he never had the chance to tell the Emperor the Good News of Jesus face to face, although it was pointed out that if he'd gone on to announce that Jesus was really the supreme ruler of the world, so therefore he (Nero) wasn't, the outcome of the hearing may have been quite different! Thanks to Paul's time in the city, the Roman church developed a solid foundation, with increasing numbers of people joining it from all levels of society. There was a growing, if grudging, recognition by the civic authorities that having lots of Christians in the city helped them tackle a range of issues, including poverty and crime. In the business world, the integrity of the Christians was generating both admiration and amazement, as bribery and corruption seem to have previously been the cultural norm.

Once a free man again, Paul wasted no time planning his next journeys. He had long wanted to visit Crete, in particular, as well as some of the other islands where there were groups of believers. First, he said, he would go west to Hispania province, while he was relatively near, and then come back to Rome before heading east again. He and I agreed, not without a great deal of sadness, that it was the time for the parting of our ways. Life on the road no longer appealed to me, although a short sea journey was still something I'd be willing to undertake. Paul again suggested that I might like to return to Corinth, where we both had plenty of friends. It was time he wrote to the likes of Stephanas and Crispus again – I could take the letter with me. If, in due course, he knew that he'd be in Rome for any length of time, he'd send word to me.

A few weeks later Paul, John Mark and several of the others travelled with me to the port of Puteoli. There I booked a passage to Corinth by way of Rhegium. Remembering my own misgivings about the reputation of Corinth before our first visit there, I was surprised at how much I was looking forward to returning. While at Puteoli, Paul intended to make enquiries about vessels that might be heading for Hispania. As we all said our farewells on the quayside, I was quite unable to keep the tears from my eyes. I knew that, for any number of possible reasons, we were unlikely to meet again in this world.

As the wind filled our sails and the harbourside buildings dwindled into the distance, my mind began to revisit the strange sequence of events that had resulted in my life becoming so improbably full of unforgettable adventures. If only I was a real storyteller!

What Shall I Read Next?

Recommendations from the Publisher

It's Me: Jesus
David J. Aston
ISBN 978-1-910197-25-7

The four gospels retold as Jesus might have told the story himself.

Join him on a journey of friendship, laughter, revelation and hardships. Follow him on the donkey into Jerusalem. Listen as he talks about the creation. Watch as he restores people to health and wholeness. Accompany him on the hard road to the cross.

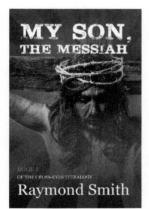

My Son, the Messiah
Raymond Smith
ISBN 978-1-910197-01-1

Throughout the whole Roman Empire, it was what every mother dreaded: crouching at the foot of a wooden stake, waiting for your son to breathe his last and to bring an end to hours of excruciating pain and torture.

As well as the usual feelings that somehow it was wrong that the child should die before his mother, there was the confusion as to why my son, my firstborn, should be in that awful situation. Why was he being treated as a criminal? And not just any criminal, but on a par with insurrectionists?

"How long?" was in everybody's thoughts, if not on their lips…

Books available from all good bookshops or directly from the publisher:

www.onwardsandupwards.org